Table of contents

KU-718-613

Acknowledgements

The scientific research project, *Engineering Historic Futures: Adapting Historic Environments to Moisture-Related Climate Change* was funded by the Engineering and Physical Sciences Research Council (EPSRC) under the Environment and Infrastructure Programme, Building Knowledge for Climate Change. We are grateful for the support of the Engineering and Physical Sciences Research Council and the UK Climate Impacts Programme, for their practical assistance throughout the project and for their vision for stakeholder participation.

It seems therefore appropriate to acknowledge the benefits that have accrued to the scientific researchers from the thoughtful participation of heritage, commercial and industry stakeholders: Ecclesiastical Insurance, English Heritage, Historic Scotland, Munters Dehumdification Ltd and The National Trust. In particular, we should like to record our thanks to the late Dr Nigel J. Seeley, former Head of Conservation at The National Trust and latterly Visiting Professor at the UCL Centre for Sustainable Heritage for his unstinting support at the inception of the project. With his early demise, the project was robbed of his wise counsel. Finally, we should like to record the generosity of English Heritage, whose financial support has made possible the publication of this stakeholder dissemination report.

Professor May Cassar
UCL Centre for Sustainable Heritage
University College London
January 2007

An electronic version of this report can be downloaded at
www.ucl.ac.uk/sustainableheritage/publications.htm

For further information on this and other research please contact:
m.cassar@ucl.ac.uk

Executive summary

Engineering Historic Futures is one of a portfolio of research projects funded by the Engineering and Physical Sciences Research Council (EPSRC) under the overall programme of Building Knowledge for a Changing Climate (BKCC) which looks at how climate change will affect different aspects of the built environment. The project is promoted jointly by EPSRC and the UK Climate Impacts Programme (UKCIP).

The specific remit of the Engineering Historic Futures Project was to gain an increased understanding of the wetting properties and drying processes of historic masonry walls, specifically those constructed of brick and sandstone. The main project outcome was intended to be the development of a computer model that can predict how long masonry walls, of these two most commonly found traditional methods of construction take to dry under different conditions of external climate, room temperature and relative humidity.

In order to achieve this, the three year project, which has been managed by UCL Centre for Sustainable Heritage, combined the investigation of two case studies together with laboratory experiments and the application of computer simulation modelling.

The case studies undertaken by Glasgow Caledonian University were carried out at Blickling Hall in Norfolk, a brick built Grade 1 listed early 17th century mansion, owned by The National Trust and Brodick Castle, a sandstone Category A listed building dating back to the 13th century on the Isle of Arran, in the care of The National Trust for Scotland.

Two test walls, one in brick and one in sandstone, were constructed in an environmental chamber at Glasgow Caledonian University to match as closely as possible the walls at the case study sites.

The Engineering Historic Futures project brought together five stakeholders all of whom have an interest in the conservation and repair of historic buildings and the likely impacts of climate change.

The National Trust which is a charity and completely independent of Government has 3.4 million members and 43,000 volunteers and protects over 300 historic houses and gardens as well as numerous other sites of national importance.

English Heritage, the UK Government's advisory body for the built heritage has more than 400 historic sites in its guardianship, including Stonehenge and Hadrian's Wall.

Historic Scotland is an Agency within the Scottish Executive Education Department and is directly responsible to Scottish Ministers for safeguarding the nation's historic environment, and promoting its understanding and enjoyment.

Munters Limited is the leading company in the temporary drying and control of temperature and humidity levels in all types of buildings and provided the de-humidification equipment for the case study investigations.

Ecclesiastical Insurance Group plc is the leading insurer of historic buildings in the UK insuring virtually every Anglican Church and Cathedral. Ecclesiastical is involved as insurer either in whole or in part with a third of the World Heritage Sites in the UK and has played a major part in the repair and restoration of churches following such events as the flooding of Lewes in October 2000, Boscastle in August 2004 and Carlisle in January 2005.

Two Stakeholder Dissemination workshops were also held, one in Glasgow and one in London during September 2006 which provided the opportunity for all those with an interest in historic buildings to comment on the research.

Much was learned from the project, although it also highlighted the difficulties and limitations of research in this area.

On the positive side there is much to give comfort to those with the responsibility for maintaining historic buildings. Thick masonry walls have a high moisture content anyway and are inherently wet to a greater or lesser degree. Historic masonry walls are of "breathable construction" and have the ability to absorb and then evaporate moisture. Provided the foundations are not permanently saturated by standing water, current rainfall predictions do not indicate significant changes in driving rain effects on the moisture content or performance of historic masonry walls.

Whilst we expect to experience more "torrential" rainfall events across the country, often in the order of 100 mm of rain in one hour, summers in the longer term (2070–2099) are likely to become drier. The internal conditions of buildings, starting with the internal surfaces of walls (which may include wall paintings) are likely to become drier.

The research emphasises the importance of good housekeeping and natural control measures. The benefits of natural ventilation cannot be stressed too greatly. The research has shown that restricting the rates of natural ventilation internally can increase the moisture content of the air by up to 40%. There is a general consensus that "forced drying" should not be used in the context of historic buildings. Whilst this may bring about a rapid reduction in the moisture content at the surface, the bulk of the wall remains wet, irrespective of the external conditions, and there is a potential risk of causing damage to vulnerable parts of the building fabric.

Although not originally intended as a part of the research, the measurements at Brodick Castle highlighted the effects on moisture content of the failure of lead guttering. Adequate and well maintained rainwater disposal systems remain at the heart of the protection of historic buildings, and epitomise the need for effective building maintenance.

A number of issues remain to be resolved. The computer model which was developed to test out different drying scenarios is necessarily complex and therefore not a tool suitable for non-scientists. As highlighted by a number of the stakeholders each building is unique and the number of environmental variables that would need to be monitored such as wind speed and direction, solar radiation, temperature, and exact nature of wall construction makes the construction of a model to cater for all circumstances a highly involved process.

The next stage of development should take into account datasets of these variables rather than relying solely on weather files.

Overall, however, the project has given us some valuable data and provided a solid foundation on which to base further research.

Chris Hawkings
Senior Surveyor
Ecclesiastical Insurance Group plc

Stakeholder comments

Ecclesiastical Insurance

Ecclesiastical Insurance provides cover against storm, lightning and flood damage for a wide range of historic buildings from churches and cathedrals to secular buildings of all kinds including schools and country houses. It is of vital importance that we understand the nature of these buildings and the materials used in their construction. Not only do we wish to give advice to our customers regarding the maintenance of their buildings but we need to know how best to deal with repairs and restoration when damage occurs. It is for these reasons that we are so supportive of this project.

Our environmental policy underlines this commitment. Ecclesiastical Insurance recognises that its activities impact upon the environment both through its internal operations and its influence and effects on the wider community. We are committed to the protection of the environment and a process of continual improvement in our environmental performance and pollution prevention.

It is now generally accepted that global warming is fact and one does not have to look far to find examples of apparently record weather events, both in the UK and abroad. As insurers we see the effects of climate change at first hand and the misery and devastation it causes to both individuals and businesses. As well as the damage to buildings themselves we see people having to leave their homes while repairs are undertaken and the loss of businesses which may have taken years to establish.

However, memories are short and it is rarely difficult to find even more extreme examples in the records. The Birmingham tornado of July 2005 was undoubtedly severe but locals in the worst affected Mosely district remember a tornado of 25 years previously. Neither can we say the tornado was due to exceptional heat – it was no more than a pleasant summer's day.

We do, however, seem to be seeing localised summer 'torrential' rainfall events across the country, often in the order of 100 mm of rain in one hour. This causes water run-off problems, with water running off a hill, through a back door and then out of the front door, regardless of the presence of watercourses. Drains are often unable to cope, with consequent backing up and overflow of toilets and sewers.

Extensive flooding across Yorkshire in June 2005 was the result of a typical summer flash flood. Press reports talked about widespread devastation and the resultant damage to the local tourist industry. However, those of us with long memories will say that events like Boscastle in 2004 have happened in the past. Examples include the Lynton & Lynmouth flood disaster of August 1952, when 34 lives were lost, and flooding that persisted for several weeks across Somerset in May 1979. What is certain, however, is that similar events will continue to happen in the future and almost certainly with increasing frequency.

Summer drought leading to subsidence damage also seems to be on the increase and once again in 2006 we are perilously close to an 'event' year for this type of claim with hosepipe bans being introduced to the South-East as early as April. The frequency pattern (1976, 1985, 1989, 1990, 1991, 1995, 1996, 2003) appears to be speeding up, making it all the more important to manage the risk. More than 80% of cases are caused by tree root related clay shrinkage and many could be avoided by timely and prudent tree management programmes. Unfortunately, little thought is given to this problem in periods of wetter weather, when trees flourish and grow rapidly. Most building owners are pleased to see leafy streets without giving any thought to the unseen roots spreading beneath the foundations.

It would seem that we are heading for hotter drier summers interspersed with bursts of torrential rainfall and perhaps more frequent and severe wind-storms. We are unable to change the location of these events but individuals and organisations can take basic precautions by managing their trees and making sure that roofs, gutters and drains are maintained.

The importance of maintaining natural ventilation within a building should not be underestimated. The research has shown that natural ventilation has a considerable effect in reducing moisture content within a building thus reducing the effect of moisture ingress. A properly maintained wall, paying particular attention to the maintenance of mortar joints and lead flashings, should perform well in keeping moisture out even with a high level of rainfall.

Whilst forced drying has a more powerful and immediate effect, conditions will quickly return to the previous state once mechanical intervention is removed.

Whilst there is more work to be done, the initial findings of Engineering Historic Futures do seem to provide us with some comfort regarding the sustainability of our historic buildings. These buildings have already survived for hundreds of years. We need to ensure that measures are in place to ensure survival for the next hundred years and beyond. Whilst their walls are inherently wet we need to ensure adequate internal ventilation, that gutters and down-pipes are of sufficient size and that surrounding drainage works are such that water can be removed without walls becoming totally saturated.

Whilst stone appears to be a more resilient material than brick, provided walls are well constructed and maintained they should keep moisture out of a building under the conditions predicted for the future. It is not so much the materials themselves we need to concern ourselves with, but rather the mechanisms in place for the removal and dispersal of water following bursts of torrential rain.

It is not just attention to the buildings themselves which concerns us but the need to have contingency plans already in place to deal with a disaster when it happens. Whether it is called Disaster Recovery Planning or Business Continuity Planning it is incumbent upon the owner of every historic building to have worked out in advance how they will deal with a severe weather event causing flood, storm or other damage so that the effects of this on the structure can be minimised and the work that goes on in the building can continue. If the business itself fails then there may no longer be the income with which to ensure the building's survival.

Despite predicted climate change, provided the measures outlined above are put into effect, we should be able to minimise its effect on insurance claims and provide some stability to the cost of insurance.

English Heritage

As the UK Government's advisory body for the built heritage, English Heritage is committed to supporting research which attempts to increase our understanding of the wetting and drying of in situ buildings. For materials ranging from brick and timber to concrete and metal, and structures ranging from single-room cob houses to complex buildings composed of many different materials (Blickling Hall is an excellent example), moisture remains the critical driver for most deterioration. How can we best prevent problems, and (where this is impossible) how can we best treat damage?

Through the projections published by UKCIP, the Government paints a picture of the ways in which the UK climate seems likely to change over the coming 80 years. Most historic buildings were designed before the ubiquitous use of fossil fuels, and so seem likely to be well-suited to a low-carbon economy, but the strong possibility that extreme events will become stronger and more common is of great concern. It raises the spectre of frequent flooding – not only ground flooding, but flooding caused by the failure of roofs and rainwater disposal systems. Increasingly English Heritage is being asked "What is the best way of drying my flooded building?" and "How long will it take for my building to dry?"

These were the questions driving the Engineering Historic Futures research, and although we have not perhaps arrived at conclusive answers, the project has highlighted important gaps in our knowledge, and pointed towards ways of resolving these. For example, it is clearly important that we find reliable ways of monitoring moisture in walls, not least to see how closely theory ties in with reality.

One particularly interesting and useful result of the project was the pattern of drying revealed by the laboratory test walls. It was possible to see that using forced drying meant the surface dried quickly, but after this the bulk of the wall remained wet, whatever the external conditions. This is in perfect accord with the current theories of drying, which suggest a two-stage process: the first stage being drying by liquid transfer to the surface, and the second (which begins when the liquid water path begins to break up) drying by vapour transfer. The former is very fast and effective, and governed by the ambient conditions of evaporation; the latter is extremely slow, and almost independent of the ambient conditions (being governed instead by the porous structure of the wall). In this experiment we have confirmation that rapid drying produces a temporary and superficial result, which is detrimental to the long-term drying of the wall. This is better supported by slow and steady drying, prolonging Stage 1 as long as possible.

Our current approach to drying focuses on getting the building re-occupied as quickly as possible, but these results suggest that changes may be necessary, and such changes may well have far-reaching socio-economic implications. Future research could usefully address practical questions such as: "Is it better to remove a permeable plaster, or to leave it in place?", and more intangible issues such as "How wet can the bulk of a wall be before the building becomes unacceptable for occupation?"

Another interesting and important result arose from the laboratory and site investigations of driving rain. Opinions had been long divided as to whether or not driving drain was able to penetrate solid masonry walls. It is now clear that in the absence of another sink of moisture in the wall, driving rain is absorbed only by the surface pores, from which it is quickly lost again by evaporation. If, however, liquid water has been able to enter the fabric by some other route – at Brodick Castle it was leakages through the parapet walkway – then the driving rain will be added to the liquid flow path, and can indeed travel rapidly through even the thickest wall.

This result highlights another important problem that arose during the research: each site is unique, and we do not yet understand real walls and real buildings well enough to confidently develop models that could take the place of *in situ* monitoring and measurement. Models may have some potential for examining our theories of wetting and drying, but for the foreseeable future they will not be useful diagnostic tools for real buildings.

Historic Scotland

As an Executive Agency of the Scottish Ministers with the function of advising them on all matters relating to the built heritage, Historic Scotland must remain in the forefront of conservation knowledge by supporting research into all conservation issues including the impacts of climate change on historic buildings. Tourism, largely founded on Scotland's built heritage in its widest sense, continues to be the country's principal industry and thus crucial to her future development.

The greater part of Scotland is classified as an area of moderate to extreme exposure. Traditional forms of construction have evolved since earliest times to withstand the rigours of the climate using indigenous sources of stone, earth and, later, brick all built with lime mortar and finished with lime harl. Natural slate and thatch provided durable and readily-renewable roof coverings. These materials gave walls the ability to absorb and then evaporate moisture, so-called "breathable construction". Would this natural mechanism be able to deal with changes in rainfall and storminess if climate change predictions hold true? Despite the proven performance of such materials moisture penetration has for long been a significant problem for many rural and certain urban buildings. Tower houses and castles, customarily located on exposed sites, are particularly prone to water penetration problems especially where their original construction or later maintenance is of poor quality. Saturated walls in all dwellings and other building types present hazards to the health and comfort of the occupants, and reduce the thermal insulation values of masonry walls. Nevertheless mass wall construction continued through the eras of "polite" urban architecture and into the early 20th century and has proved successful, though dependant on good levels of building maintenance.

Predictions of climate change over the next 100 years indicate extreme variations in weather patterns and, particularly, increased rainfall and flooding, higher average temperatures and increased frequency of storms across Scotland. These changes will impact on Scotland's traditional buildings by inducing enhanced rates of natural decay; on her inland archaeology by riverine flooding, and flooding of coastal sites through rising sea levels; and on her landscape by changes in vegetation growth and soil erosion. The natural drying-out of saturated walls or flooded buildings, frequently requiring many months, is often now subject to commercial and insurance pressures to restore habitable conditions rapidly. This may lead to unforeseen failure in the physical and chemical composition of materials.

In the UCL submission to EPSRC for financial support the proposed research was limited for funding reasons to the mitigation of water ingress, and drying-out, to assess and define moisture-related problems on the fabric and contents of historic buildings, and lastly, to develop appropriate prediction tools and extrapolate from historic records to assess moisture movement and drying in historic buildings. Ultimately the research programme centred on the effects of flooding and wind-driven rain on historic structures. Historic Scotland was happy to endorse these areas of investigation, and participated throughout the three-year programme, providing practical assistance in the selection of the Scottish field test site and in the preparation and specifications for laboratory test walls in sandstone and brick.

Outturns

The EHF research has produced useful data on the performance of stone and brick walls in terms of their capacity to absorb and release moisture under natural and laboratory test conditions. Computer modelling attempted to understand how climate change will affect buildings in the future, but suffered a number of limitations including a lack of advanced knowledge of the physical characteristics of historic building materials; the complex mechanics of moisture transport and external influences on its performance; technical difficulties in moisture measuring, and the effects of ventilation on moisture movement within walls. It was thus only able to offer some broad conclusions. There will be little change in the conditions of either sandstone or brick walls in the future. More rapid movement of salts in porous brickwork will occur, but possibly less surface salt efflorescence in sandstone. Sandstone was also shown to be less susceptible to water penetration to the inner wall surface than porous brick, as water transport is more rapid despite the far higher incidence of driving rain on the sandstone case study.

Of the two field test sites Brodick Castle is of more direct relevance to the Scottish situation than Blickling Hall, and the environmental monitoring of the tower and indoor climate produced some valuable data on the performance of exposed sandstone walls. It was found that external climate influences, internal conditions in unheated buildings and in the absence of natural ventilation, internal temperature and vapour pressure will rise relative to external conditions, and the moisture content of the air will rise by up to 40%. Therefore higher air exchange rates internally will reduce the effects of moisture ingress through stone walls. Algal growth was initially recorded and increased significantly with the withdrawal of ventilation from the test room. However, other factors must be taken into account, including the porosity of the stone in any specific building; exposure and orientation (the west wall experienced twice the quantity of rainfall as the east); the condition of the masonry, in particular, the mortar joints which may allow water to enter the walls; and the overall effectiveness of maintenance of the building. At Brodick a faulty gutter complicated the accurate recording of wall moisture content.

The scientific research which produced the data leading to these conclusions was extensive and thorough, and the results and broad conclusions confirm the causes and effects of water penetration problems in existing historic buildings with which building and conservation practitioners are familiar.

The value to Historic Scotland of the Blickling test site is in the monitoring and evaluation of natural and forced drying-out by dehumidification after flooding. This is of real relevance to the treatment of flooded and saturated buildings everywhere. That said, the external wall of the basement test site was continuously saturated during the programme due to being partially below external ground level – not a very frequent situation – and only those dowels inserted above external soil level showed less than the maximum reading of about 30% moisture content. As at Brodick, removal of the existing free air circulation within the room exacerbated the internal readings, resulting in a temperature increase, and a rise in air moisture content of about 20%. Wall surfaces remained constantly saturated and dowels situated at low level in the wall core registered maximum moisture content. The introduction of forced drying by dehumidification reduced the moisture content to match the external readings and wall surfaces began to dry out, reaching a new equilibrium after 40-50days. Deep moisture readings in the wall showed a similar moisture reduction. However, cessation of dehumidification after more than 100 days in use caused the original basement conditions to return.

In general the findings here confirmed those at Brodick. Altering internal conditions affects measurements on and within external walls. Most significant is the value of ventilation and dehumidification to control surface and deep-wall moisture content. However this is of little practical use unless the external walls are maintained in sound condition.

The purpose of laboratory testing of sandstone and brick walls was to allow controlled conditions to be applied in the wetting and drying cycles which were impossible on site. Wall construction replicated as closely as possible the two case study buildings, although carbonation of lime mortars was only partially achieved in the time available. The length of the programme and the small size of the test walls (at about 1m by 1m and limited by the capacity of the environmental chamber), resulted in some restrictions on the testing processes. Thus, realistic comparisons between forced (dehumidification) and natural drying-out of flooded walls was limited to 50 days and the results indicated that a much longer period of several months is required. The driving rain tests on the sandstone wall suggest that the amount of water absorbed is limited by its surface absorption characteristics, and the conditions within the wall core near to the inner wall face are largely unaffected. Here the differing physical characteristics of sandstones and other types of material will govern the depth of saturation within walls. The findings therefore highlight the limitations of research into one only stone type. The condition of the wall also plays a major part in its ability to deal with driving rain, and a lack of effective building maintenance is shown to be crucial to its performance. That said, the research indicates that a well-constructed and well maintained wall will keep moisture out of a building under present climatic conditions and those predicted for the future.

Conclusion

With the benefit of hindsight it may be said that even the limited scope of the research was too ambitious within the three-year period of the programme. Fundamental results were achieved in the assessment of the performance of stone and brick walls in conditions of wind-driven rain and flooding respectively, but were diluted by restrictions of programme time, the condition of each building as found, and some lack of available data on building materials characteristics. Whilst it would be unrealistic to test every type of wall construction under the two regimes adopted here there is clearly much scope for further research to lead to pragmatic guidance for the mitigation of future climate change impacts.

The broad conclusion indicates that the walls of the Scottish case study are likely to withstand forecast future increased precipitation, and this is welcome news to conservation practitioners and building owners alike. However, without further research, it is difficult to apply these conclusions too generally as the composition and performance of building stones and mortars varies considerably across Scotland.

Munters Ltd

The effects of climate change will in the long term have a significant impact on the Damage Management industry. Increased risks of flooding, frequency of storms and summer droughts will bring about a change in the way the loss management business is currently shaped.

As a stakeholder in the Engineering Historic Futures research project which was funded by the Engineering and Physical Science Research Council it was with great anticipation and excitement that we commenced on a path that would hopefully provide us with much more detailed information on the impacts of climate change on the built heritage.

In order to provide us with important information a drying model was developed using a small number of heritage sites. The key was to look at the different ways materials reacted when subjected to quite different environmental conditions.

Model development and application

The Canute model was developed and compared with other building simulation and heat and moisture models, including costs and energy consumption of the drying intervention.

This model application was used on the wall fabric of the type at Blickling Hall and Brodick Castle using high resolution weather scenario data from another EPSRC-funded research project, 'Built Environment: Weather scenarios for investigation of Impacts and Extremes (BETWIXT)' from the same programme, 'Building Knowledge for Climate Change'.

The Blickling Hall case study monitored the effect (if any) of floor-to-ceiling and wall-to-wall partitioning on room climate and wall conditions, the effect (if any) of removal of wall render on wall moisture content, and the effect of dehumidification on wall and room environment. Costs and energy consumption of the drying intervention were also considered.

The Brodick Castle case study monitored the effect (if any) of partitioning on room climate and wall conditions and made a comparison between the west and east wall conditions. The role of a fault in the parapet and driving rain in the wetting of the west wall as well as the conditions that led to algae growth on the west wall also needed to be considered.

Moisture content measurements led to a discussion of dowel resistivity measurements and their success and failures. This led to some questions on the use of dowels for moisture measurement in masonry and a discussion of moisture measurement techniques for internal masonry walls.

Laboratory test wall experiments required background research on wall materials and construction methods, a comparison of reconstructed and historic walls and between natural and forced drying after flooding of a replica brick wall, and a discussion of the extent of water penetration into the replica stone wall during spraying experiments and the implications for driving rain.

The outcome of all of this work is detailed in the scientific reports that follow. The contents combine such subjects as quantifying the costs of climate impacts on the built heritage and realistic methods of measuring moisture in materials.

The question is having looked at all the information contained in all of the reports and documentation, will it bring about a change in methodology of loss management companies? My answer is that it has to, given the dwindling stock of buildings of historic significance which will be hit hard by climate related impacts.

The social and economic effects of climate change do force the catalyst for change. This can be looked at in a number of different ways. It could be, in fact, the method that is used to ensure a building is dried correctly, even if it means just letting natural drying taking place when external conditions are suitable.

I believe that the phrase forced drying should not be used in context of drying historic buildings. A better way of explaining the way forward is bringing the building back to a state of equilibrium in order to prevent further damage occurring. The speed of this return should be viewed together with the information gathered during this project.

A more sympathetic approach is vital for the future of each affected building.

Regularity of flooding or wetting will also impact the material stability. The modeling does take this into account to some degree, however, it is extremely hard to simulate degradation over a fifty- or hundred-year timeframe.

Many loss management companies already have the skills to identify some of the complex issues involved in the restoration of flooded historic buildings. However, with the information and data gathered during the three-year programme, this will provide invaluable help in prolonging the life of historic buildings.

The National Trust

This statement summarises the perspective of The National Trust, one of Britain's foremost heritage management organisations on the Engineering Historic Futures project.

What our needs are?

The Trust is concerned about the increasing incidence of flooding and water penetration problems in our historic properties which is likely to be a consequence of global climate change. These incidents have been caused by flooding from river overflows or sea surges, urban and rural water run-off from inadequate surface drainage and increased severe rainfall and storminess.

The effect of these incidents on historic properties has caused flooding of basements and ground floor rooms, roof leaks, overflowing of rainwater goods and damp penetration through window surrounds and walls. In order to deal in a more effective way with the problems caused by water penetration in historic properties, the Trust needs to find reliable methods for monitoring moisture in masonry walls, suitable techniques for the drying out of flood affected walls, a better understanding of the wetting and drying properties of different wall materials and a model for predicting the wetting and drying behaviour of different masonry walls.

The Trust's expectations of the research were to develop a better understanding of the dynamic movement of water through flooded brick and stone wall structures, an understanding of how drying works and differs for different building fabrics, experimental brick and stone walls which would be effective proxies for the behaviour of the two test wall sites in response to wetting and drying interventions, the establishment of a wetting and drying model for historic buildings and the establishment of best practice guidelines for drying out of buildings in the event of a flood or water ingress.

Comments on the findings

The results were seriously hampered by a moisture sampling technique (electrical resistance measurements) which was inadequate for walls with high saturation and they did not provide a deeper understanding of the dynamic nature of water movement in masonry. Trialling other comparative assisted drying methods apart from dehumidification could have been considered, such as forced air ventilation. The results from the model have been encouraging, but in its present form it has not been able to provide a complete picture, in part due to the complexity of historic buildings compared with modern buildings.

The way forward

Further research should be focused on the following areas to build on the experiences of Engineering Historic Futures:

- Improved methods for monitoring moisture within the building fabric
- The development of methods of monitoring the equilibrium moisture state of buildings
- Understanding the relationship between moisture content and deterioration of materials under moisture induced stress
- Work on a simplified model for non-specialists which is able to predict likely behaviour based on an understanding of certain key parameters

1 Blickling Hall basement case study

Paul H. Baker,[1] Chris Sanders,[1] Graham H. Galbraith[1] and R. Craig McLean[2]

[1]Glasgow Caledonian University, [2]Strathclyde University

© NT. Fisheye Images

Introduction

Blickling Hall, Norfolk, was selected as a suitable case study for field monitoring as part of the Engineering Historic Futures project, with the objective of collecting data for the validation of a hygrothermal model. The basement area, which was chosen for monitoring, has a history of flooding and suffers from severe algae problems (Figure 1) and salt damage (Figure 2). The construction of the basement walls consists of approximately 700mm thick clay brick and lime mortar walls, lined partly with a cementitious tanking from floor level and lime plaster higher up the wall. The south-west facing wall (Figure 2), which has a window with the sill just above ground level, was chosen for monitoring moisture contents using wooden dowels. Wall surface and room temperatures and relative humidities were measured. Climate data were collected using a weather station in the grounds of the Hall. Soil moisture contents were also measured in the area outside the basement for part of the monitoring period.

Figure 1 North-east wall of basement

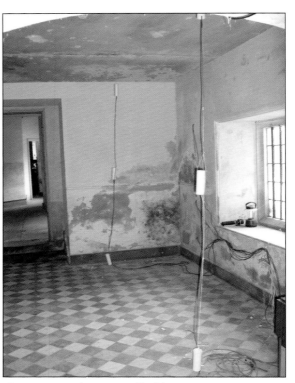

Figure 2 South-west wall of basement

This report summarises the results of the monitoring period from May 2004 to July 2006, which includes four phases as follows:

May 2004 to May 2005	Air allowed to circulate through basement area from adjacent corridors.
May 2005 to December 2005	Basement area partitioned off to reduce air exchange.
December 2005 to March 2006	The tanking and plaster were removed from a section of the wall to the right of the basement window in early December 2005. The area was enclosed and a de-humidifier was installed.
March 2006 to July 2006	Post de-humidification. The enclosure and de-humidifier were removed.

Monitoring of basement and outdoor climate

Basement

Preparations for monitoring of the basement were made between 5 and 7 May 2004.

A 25mm diameter core drilling was taken to a depth of about 420mm from a location about halfway up the wall to the left hand side of the window (Figure 3). However, the material removed was mostly powdered brick and mortar, and as such was unsatisfactory for the determination of the wall construction.

Wall moisture content

Six 12mm diameter holes (Figure 3) were drilled for the insertion of moisture sensors into the wall to a depth of approximately 450mm, which corresponds to the internal edge of the window frame, as agreed with the NT house manager for Blickling. The position of the holes in the wall on the left hand side of the window was approximately mid-way between the edge of the window opening and the corner of the wall with the internal partition wall; i.e. about 630mm from the left hand edge of the window opening. Similarly, the holes on the right hand side were drilled at 630mm from the right hand edge of the window opening. The approximate thickness of the wall is 700mm. The holes were chosen to represent the following locations:

The lower profiles (370mm above floor level) where the wall is below soil level, which is just below the window sill;

The middle profiles (930mm and 890mm above floor level at LHS and RHS, respectively) where the wall is above soil level, and may be prone to flooding;

The upper profiles (1960mm and 1930mm above floor level at LHS and RHS, respectively) where the wall is above soil level, but is unlikely to experience flooding.

The material drilled out of the wall was a mixture of dry and wet brick and mortar. Some of the drillings consisted of a wet putty-like material. Overall, the general inhomogenous nature of the drillings indicated that the wall probably has a brick and mortar rubble fill.

The moisture content sensors were made from 40mm lengths of 10mm diameter dowelling. The electrical resistance of each dowel was measured by means of stainless steel screws inserted through terminals at each end of the dowel. The terminals were made from insulated copper wire soldered onto washers. Heat-shrink sleeving was shrunk around each end of the dowel and used as former for a resin compound in order to provide a seal for the terminal assembly. Figure 4 shows a completed sensor. The relationship between resistance and moisture content of the dowel has been established by laboratory calibration using a Protimeter timber moisture content metre. The relationship between the moisture content of the brick and that of the dowel is more complex and was the subject of a laboratory investigation which concluded that the dowels were capable of showing longer term trends in the condition of the wall, but not the dynamic behaviour over a shorter period due to the lag in the moisture content of the dowels behind that of the brick under wetting or drying conditions.

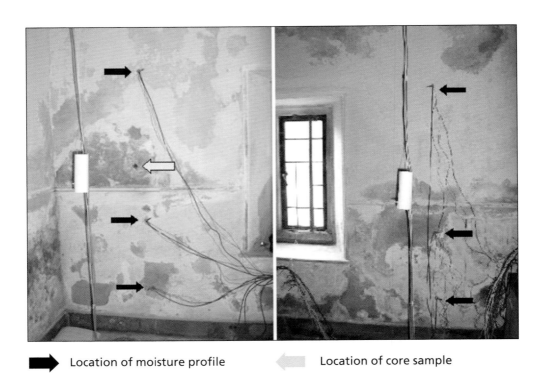

Location of moisture profile   Location of core sample

Figure 3 Location of holes drilled for core sample and moisture content profiles. Two of the radiation shields holding the basement air temperature and relative humidity sensors are also shown.

Figure 4 Original dowels used for moisture content measurement.

Figure 5 Replacement dowel with three measurement locations. Blue heat shrink sleeving is used to cover electrical connections.

The dowels were inserted into the six holes, with three sensors per profile, located at the end of the hole (*outer/location* #1), about half-way along the hole (*mid/location* #2) and near the wall surface (*inner/location* #3). The dowels were separated by lengths of nylon rod and balls of flexible sealant. The original dowels were replaced by new dowels of a different design on 26 May 2006. The latter consisted of single 500mm lengths of 9mm diameter dowelling with three measurement positions, as for the original dowels, along the length of each dowel (Figure 5). Heat-shrink sleeving was shrunk around sections of the dowel to protect the electrical connections and also to give a snug fit when driven into the 12mm diameter holes.

Environmental conditions

Temperatures and relative humidities were measured, using combined temperature and humidity sensors, at six locations in the basement in two floor-to-ceiling profiles approximately 1 metre in front of the locations of the moisture content profiles each side of the window. The sensors were mounted inside radiation shields (Figure 3).

Interior wall surface temperature and relative humidity sensors were located near to the locations of the moisture content profiles (Figure 3). Temperature and relative humidity sensors were also mounted at two locations on the surface of the exterior wall (Figure 6).

A programmable stand-alone data logger (Delta-T Devices DL2e) was used. Logging commenced at 10:00h 7 May 2004. All sensors were logged at 1 minute intervals and hourly average data were saved. Occasional logging problems were encountered which resulted in missing data periods.

Soil moisture content

Using a Campbell Scientific CR10X data logger with three CS616 water content reflectometers, the soil moisture content in the flowerbed outside the basement window was measured in three locations (Figure 9). The CS616 is designed to measure volumetric water content of soils or other porous media. The water content information is derived from the probe sensitivity to the dielectric constant of the medium being measured.

Readings were recorded at hourly intervals from 7 May 2004 until 26 May 2005 when the equipment was removed. The soil forms an important boundary to the basement as a source of moisture, however the fluctuations in the soil moisture content over the period were found to be small with an average soil moisture content of 46 ±2%.

Figure 6 Location of outside wall surface temperature and relative humidity sensors, and soil moisture content probe in flower bed outside basement window.

Figure 7 Blickling Hall weather station for EHF project

Weather station

The weather station (Figure 7) was installed in the walled garden at Blickling Hall on 30 March 2004.

The station comprises the following sensors:

- Air temperature and relative humidity
- Wind speed (anemometer)
- Potentiometric wind vane (wind direction)
- Sunshine sensor (global horizontal and diffuse solar radiation, and sunshine state)
- Rain gauge

All sensors are connected to a Delta-T devices DL2e logger, mounted inside a weatherproof cabinet secured to the mast. With the exception of the rain gauge and the wind vane, the sensors are logged at 1 minute intervals and recorded as hourly averages. The total rain fall is recorded every ten minutes. Spot readings of wind direction are recorded at ten minute intervals, since it is inappropriate to take averages of wind direction. The wind direction for each hour is derived by resolution of the ten minute average wind speed and the spot readings of direction.

Logging started at 13:00 on 30 March. Similar to the basement, occasional logging problems were encountered which resulted in missing data periods. The sunshine sensor was found to be unreliable for diffuse radiation and sunshine hours and failed completely during January 2006.

Interventions

Partitioning
Access to the corridor, connecting the basement to the later Victorian west wing, was sealed off on 8th May 2005 (Fig. 8). The door at other end of the basement was kept closed.

Figure 8 Partitioning of basement area from corridor

De-humidification of a section of wall

The tanking on a section of the wall on the right hand side of the window was removed on 1 December 2005 (Figure 9). (Some of the lime plaster above the tanking was also removed in error.) A polythene enclosure was fitted over that section of the wall on 9 December 2005 and connected to a de-humidifier (Figure 10). The dry air blown into the enclosure can escape between the edges of the polythene and the wall. The enclosure and the de-humidifier were removed on 23 March 2006. It should be noted that data were lost between removal of the tanking and just prior to starting the de-humidification.

Figure 9 Section of wall to right of window with tanking removed.

Figure 10 Enclosure and de-humidifier.

The monitoring ended on 26 July 2006.

Results

The results are summarised below considering each of the four phases of monitoring.
- Figures 11–14 show the basement air and external conditions over the monitoring period.
- The wall surface conditions are compared with the basement air conditions in Figures 15–20.
- Figures 21–26 present the dowel moisture contents.

Please note that major loss of data in the basement occurred over two periods as follows:

13 December 2004 to 26 January 2005

27 September 2005 to 9 December 2005.

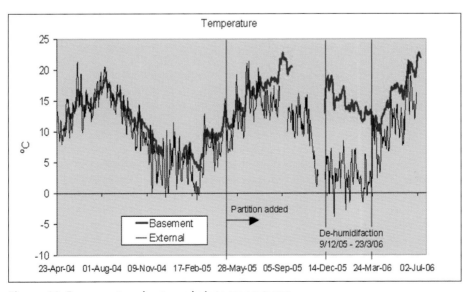
Figure 11 Basement and external air temperatures

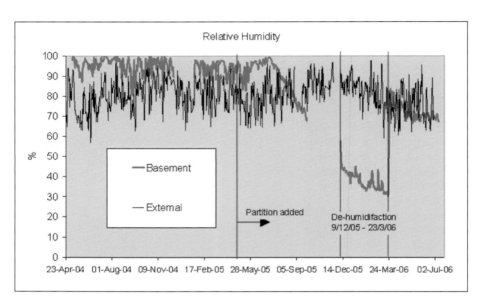

Figure 12 Basement and external relative humidities

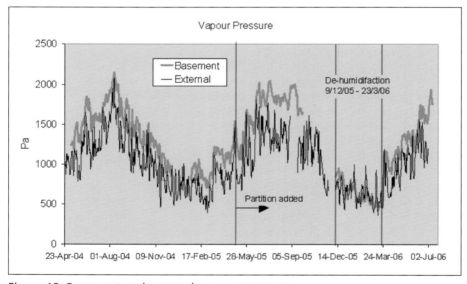

Figure 13 Basement and external vapour pressures

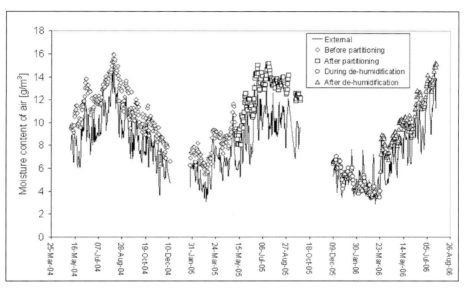

Figure 14 Moisture contents of basement and external air

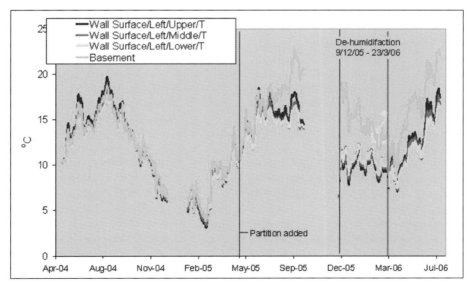

Figure 15 Wall surface temperatures on LHS of window compared to basement air temperature

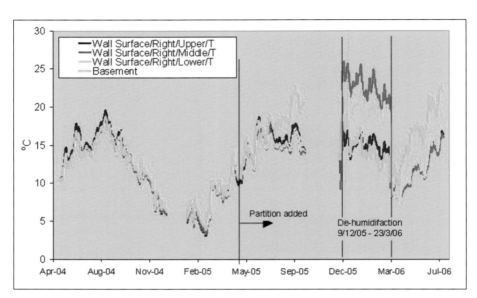

Figure 16 Wall surface temperatures on RHS of window compared to basement air temperature

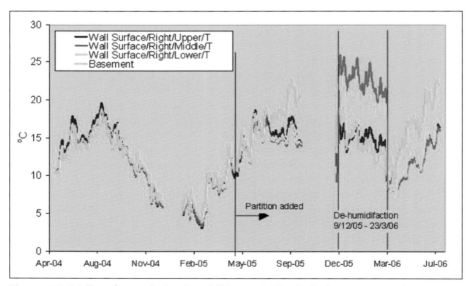

Figure 17 Wall surface relative humidities on LHS of window compared to basement air RH

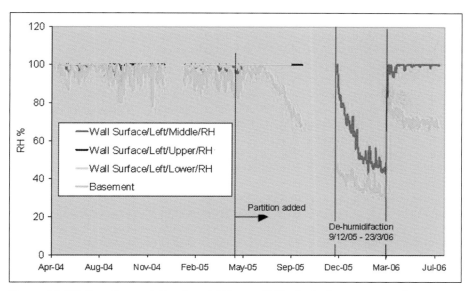

Figure 18 Wall surface relative humidities on RHS of window compared to basement air RH

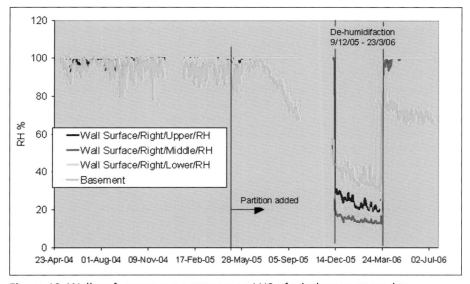

Figure 19 Wall surface vapour pressures on LHS of window compared to basement air vapour pressure

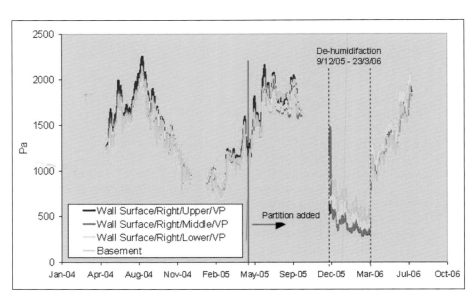

Figure 20 Wall surface vapour pressures on LHS of window compared to basement air vapour pressure

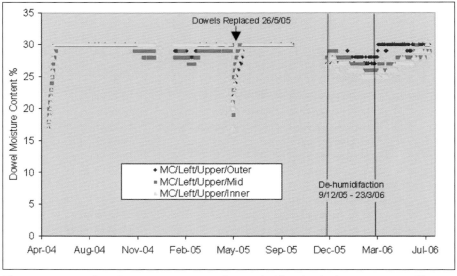

Figure 21 Dowel Moisture Contents: Left Hand Side of Window/Upper Profile

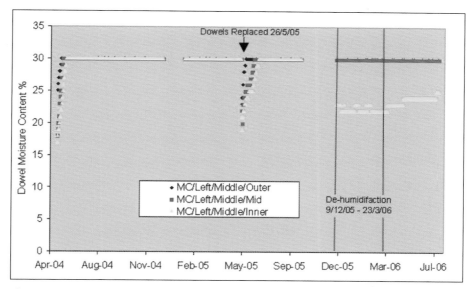

Figure 22 Dowel Moisture Contents: Left Hand Side of Window/Middle Profile

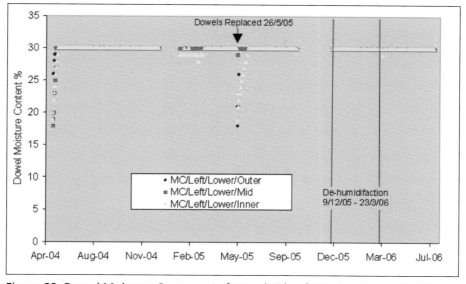

Figure 23 Dowel Moisture Contents: Left Hand Side of Window/Lower Profile

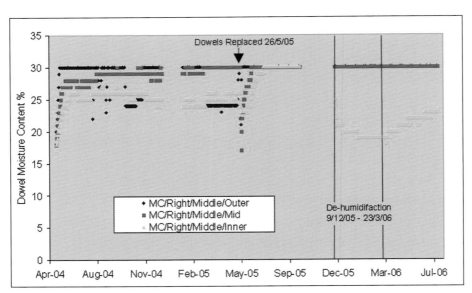

Figure 24 Dowel Moisture Contents: Right Hand Side of Window/Upper Profile

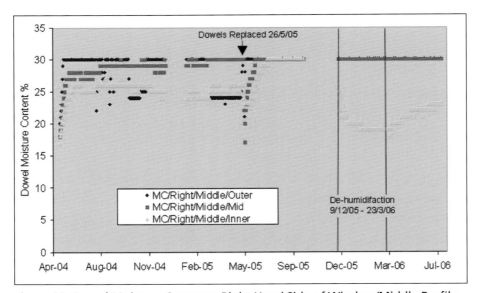

Figure 25 Dowel Moisture Contents: Right Hand Side of Window/Middle Profile

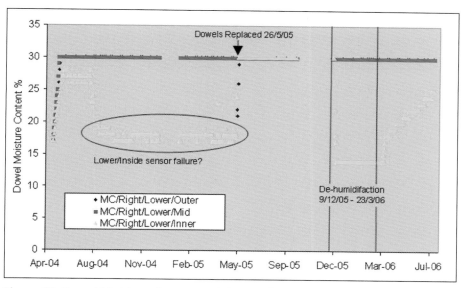

Figure 26 Dowel Moisture Contents: Right Hand Side of Window/Lower Profile

Before partitioning

Generally, the dynamic response of the basement conditions tends to follow that of the external conditions, however basement response tends to dampen out external fluctuations.

The average basement air temperature is approx. 1K higher than external temperature (Figure 11). Wall surface temperatures (Figures 15 and 16) are similar to room temperature.

The average basement relative humidity is 95% (Figure 12) and at the wall surface is >99% (Figures 17 and 18), however it is clear that both respond either directly or indirectly to fluctuations in the external conditions. This is also apparent if the vapour pressures (Figures 13, 19 and 20) and air moisture contents (Figure 14) are considered.

The average basement vapour pressure is about 280Pa (i.e. an air moisture content ~2g/m³) above external. The average surface vapour pressure is slightly higher than basement room vapour pressure by 25Pa (Figures 19 and 20). Surface vapour pressure shows more dampening of fluctuations.

Prior to the intervention, the dowels generally indicate a high moisture content (Figures 21–26) although there is some evidence that (1) the wall above ground level on RHS is drier near to the inside surface and (2) the dowels in the Mid & Outer positions of the upper LHS profile are drier.

After partitioning and before de-humidification

The room temperature rises following partitioning relative to both the external and wall temperatures. Whilst the basement relative humidity decreases, the vapour pressure increases with an average value of 440Pa (~3g/m^3) above external.

Wall surfaces remain consistently at 100% RH, thus vapour pressures are at saturation, although the average surface vapour is about 45Pa below that of the room.

After replacing the dowels during May 2005, all dowels show consistently high readings. Note, laboratory investigations using a Jacobean brick from Blickling show that the maximum dowel reading of 30% corresponds to a brick moisture content of 11% by weight at equilibrium.

De-humidification and after

Although targeted at the section of the wall with the tanking removed, the effect of the de-humidifier warms up the basement as a whole with an average temperature of 12K above external. The room relative humidity falls to an average over the intervention period of 38%. The average vapour pressure falls to below the external value. Figure 27 shows an estimated drying curve for the room based on the internal-external vapour pressure difference. A new equilibrium in the room occurs after about 50 days of de-humidification.

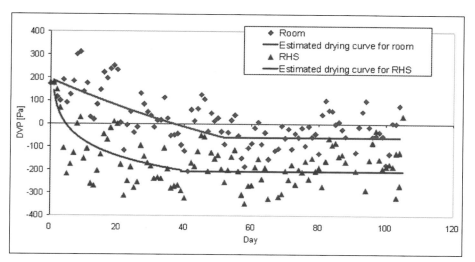

Figure 27 Room-external and RHS wall surface-external vapour pressure differences during de-humidification and estimated drying curves

After the intervention the room conditions return, after 2–3 days, to those prevalent before de-humidification .

The target wall surface (RHS) is about 5K warmer than the room temperature although Figure 16 shows temperature stratification, with lower temperatures at the upper measurement point. Relative humidities measured at the surface fell during the intervention to around 20%RH. The vapour pressure also falls below external value by average of 180Pa over intervention period. Figure 27 indicates the drying behaviour, which reaches an equilibrium after about 40 days. Following the intervention the wall surface conditions reach saturation within about 2 days.

Whilst it was not the intention to deliberately de-humidify the LHS of the wall, the changes in room conditions have affected the wall. The wall surface temperature increases relative to the external and the relative humidity gradually decreases to about 45%. However, the average vapour pressure is about 370Pa above external. After the intervention the conditions recover as for the RHS.

During the intervention dowels near RHS surface show significant drying, with some drying also evident in upper profile. After the intervention the dowel moisture contents gradually increase. This may not reflect the brick moisture contents as laboratory trials demonstrate that the dowel response not only lags behind changes in moisture content in the brick, but also shows different wetting and drying behaviour.

Conclusions

The basement area of Blickling Hall, Norfolk, was selected as a suitable case study for field monitoring as part of the Engineering Historic Futures project, with the objective of collecting data for the validation of a hygrothermal model. The basement has a history of flooding and suffers from severe algae problems and salt damage.

The monitoring period consisted of four stages:

1. Air was allowed to circulate through the basement area from adjacent corridors.
2. The basement area was partitioned off to reduce air exchange.
3. The tanking and plaster were removed from a section of wall and subsequently enclosed and de-humidified.
4. Finally, the de-humidifier and enclosure were removed.

The basement conditions prior to partitioning respond to external conditions, however the wall surface conditions remain at or near saturation due to a constant supply of moisture from the soil below the level of the basement window. The dowel moisture contents reflect the high surface humidities, generally reaching the maximum reading soon after installation, apart from some locations above the soil level.

After partitioning, reducing the free movement of air within the room exacerbates the situation in the basement. The room temperature increases and although the relative humidity decreases, the moisture content of the air increases by about 20%. The wall surfaces remain consistently saturated. All dowel locations show the maximum moisture content.

The intervention with the de-humidifier has a dramatic effect on conditions in the room by reducing the moisture content to a similar level to that of the external air. The surfaces of both the target wall and the left hand wall show significant drying out. A new equilibrium in the basement is reached after about 40–50 days of de-humidification. General, this behaviour is also reflected in the response of the dowels.

Significantly, after ceasing de-humidification, the basement conditions quickly return over a few days, to those prevalent prior to the intervention.

Whilst the basement has its own particular moisture problems resulting from a constant moisture supply, the monitoring results indicate that shifting the room conditions (e.g. reducing ventilation, introducing de-humidification) had a significant impact on the wall conditions. Whilst the intervention with de-humidification had the greatest impact, partitioning demonstrated the importance of ventilation in ameliorating the wall conditions.

2 Environmental monitoring of Brodick Castle

Paul H. Baker,[1] Chris Sanders,[1] Graham H. Galbraith[1] and R. Craig McLean[2]

[1]Glasgow Caledonian University, [2]Strathclyde University

© Crown copyright reserved Historic Scotland Images 2007

Figure 1 Brodick Castle

Introduction

Brodick Castle (Figure 1), Arran, was selected as a suitable case study for field monitoring as part of Engineering Historic Futures project. The Tower (upper right of Figure 1), which was chosen for monitoring, suffers from water ingress problems, possibly as a consequence of driving rain. The Tower was a Victorian addition to the building constructed from porous red sandstone, which laboratory measurements indicate has a high rate of moisture uptake.

Whilst evidence of fine lime putty joints in the external masonry was apparent, there had also been some use of cement mortar for repair work. The wall and ceiling plasterwork had been removed due to water damage and remedial work had been carried out on the roof timbers (Figure 2). During a preliminary

Fig. 2 Tower interior – west wall and roof

inspection in December 2003 it was observed that there was evidence of staining of floorboards and internal stone work and the presence of algae on the west wall. The other accessible walls, the east and south, appeared to be free from evidence of moisture problems. The Tower is unheated and draughty due to the exposed roof space, leaky windows and fireplace.

This report summarises the results of the monitoring period from July 2004 to February 2006. The monitoring can be divided into two phases: before and after the installation of an air barrier in April 2005 to reduce air exchange within the room, including sealing off the roof space.

Monitoring of Tower and outdoor climate

Weather station

A weather station (Figure 3) was installed in the south-west corner of the parapet around the Tower and commissioned between 30 May and 1 June 2004.

The station comprises the following sensors:

- Air temperature and relative humidity
- Wind speed (anemometer)
- Potentiometric wind vane (wind direction)
- Sunshine sensor (global horizontal and diffuse solar radiation, and sunshine hours)
- Rain gauge
- Two additional rain gauges were used to monitor driving rain using collector plates, with 0.01m² area, mounted on the east and west walls of the Tower (Figure 4).

Figure 3 Weather station south-west corner of parapet of Tower

Figure 4 Driving rain collector plate mounted on east wall of Tower

All sensors were connected to a Delta-T Devices DL2e logger, inside the Tower. With the exception of the rain gauges, wind speed and the wind vane, the sensors were logged at 1 minute intervals and recorded as hourly averages. The rain fall in each rain gauge was recorded every ten minutes.

Spot readings of wind direction were recorded at ten minute intervals, since it is inappropriate to take averages of wind direction. Wind speed was logged at 1 minute intervals and recorded as ten minute averages. The wind direction for each hour is derived by resolution of the ten minute average wind speed and the spot readings of direction thus treating wind as a vector quantity having magnitude (speed) and direction.

Logging started at 12:00 on 1 June. The readings of diffuse radiation and sunshine hours were found to be unreliable, thus only global horizontal radiation is referred to below.

Monitoring of the Tower

Initial preparations for monitoring of the Tower were made at the same time as the installation of the weather station. However, problems were experienced inserting moisture content sensors into the walls and with one of the DL2e logger cards. The moisture content sensor was redesigned for an easier fit into the holes drilled into the walls of the Tower. Installation and commissioning were completed on 4 and 5 July 2004.

Wall moisture content

Three 12mm diameter holes were drilled for the insertion of moisture sensors into each of the south, east and west walls to a depth of approximately 450mm. The positions of the holes in the east and west elevations were selected to avoid known voids or chimneys. The vertical locations were chosen as follows:

- The lower profiles are below the level of the guttering under the walkway outside the tower (Figures 5 and 6). It was observed that the drillings from the west wall were damp compared with other locations and there was anecdotal evidence of damage to the guttering at the outside of the wall at this location;
- The middle profiles – midway between upper and lower profiles;
- The upper profiles correspond to about half-height (~1.6m) of the room below ceiling joists.

The moisture content sensors consisted of 500mm lengths of 9mm diameter dowelling. The electrical resistance of each dowel was measured by means of pairs of stainless steel screws inserted at three positions along the length of the dowel (Figure 7). Insulated copper wire was wrapped around the screw heads and soldered to give a good electrical connection. Heat-shrink sleeving was shrunk around sections of the dowel to protect the electrical connections and also to give a snug fit when driven into 12mm diameter holes.

The relationship between resistance and moisture content of the dowel has been established by laboratory calibration using a Protimeter timber moisture content meter. The relationship between the moisture content of the sandstone and that of the dowel is more complex and was the subject of a laboratory investigation

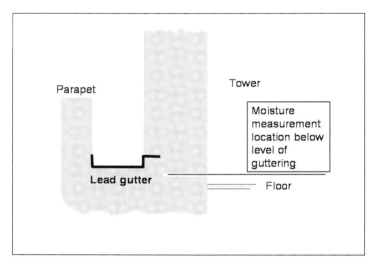

Figure 5 Schematic diagram of the location of the lower moisture content profile below gutter level

Figure 6 Photograph of the external walkway around the tower showing lead chased into stonework

which concluded that the dowels were capable of showing longer term trends in the condition of the wall, but not the dynamic behaviour over a shorter period due to the lag in the moisture content of the dowels behind that of the sandstone under wetting or drying conditions.

The three pairs of connectors per dowel are located to give readings at about $3/4$-, $1/2$- and $1/4$-way through the wall from the internal surface, *outer/location #1, mid/location #2* and *inner/location #3*, respectively.

Environmental conditions

Temperatures and relative humidities were measured, using combined temperature and humidity sensors, Honeywell type HIH-3602A at nine locations in the Tower in three floor-to-ceiling profiles in locations near the south, east and west walls. The sensors were mounted inside radiation shields.

Interior wall surface temperature and relative humidity sensors were located near to the locations of

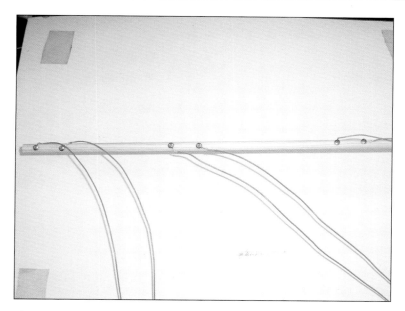

Figure 7 Moisture content sensor showing electrical connections

the upper moisture content profiles on the three walls. Temperature and relative humidity sensors were also mounted at three locations on the surface of the exterior wall. Honeywell type HIH-3610 humidity sensors were used with Fenwal Electronics 10kW thermistors.

Heat flow sensors were also surface mounted on the east and west walls although the measurements obtained were not considered to be satisfactory due to problems in achieving a good contact with the rough internal surface of the walls.

Figure 8 shows the location of some of the sensors.

Logging commenced at 17:00h 5 July 2004.

Figure 8
Location of
sensors: (left)
east and south
walls; (right)
west wall

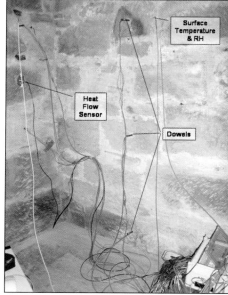

Intervention

Partitioning was installed in the Tower on the 29 April 2005, to reduce air exchange within the room. Light-weight timber studding was erected along the internal wall which divides the main room from the stairway and landing with door to parapet, and a box room in the north-west corner. A fire retardant air barrier was stapled to the studding and also to the underside of the ceiling joists (Figure 9). The layout of the room is shown in Figure 10.

Figure 9 Partitioning of the tower: (above left & middle) wall adjacent to north-west box room and stairway; (right) ceiling south-east corner.

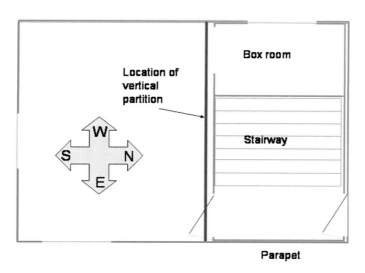

Box room

Location of
vertical
partition

Stairway

Parapet

Figure 10 Room layout indicating location of vertical partitioning

Subsequent measurements of the air leakage by a de-pressurisation test gave a $N_{50}/20$ value of 7 air changes per hour, which may be considered high. ($N_{50}/20$ is the volume air change rate measured at 50Pa pressure difference divided by 20, which has been found to give a reasonable correlation between de-pressurisation test results and actual ventilation rates under normal climate conditions.)

Results

Climate monitoring

The main climate parameters are shown in Figures 11–17 and where appropriate the corresponding conditions in the Tower, i.e. temperature, relative humidity and vapour pressure. Monthly averages or totals are given for clarity.

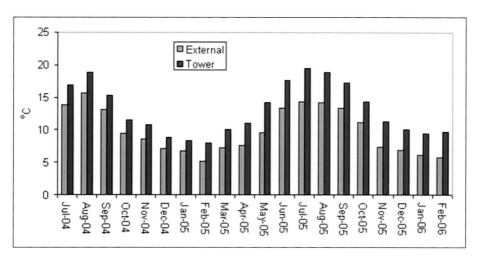

Figure 11 External and Tower air temperature

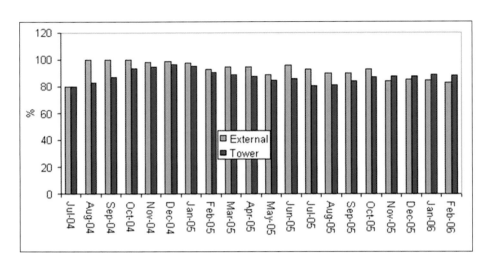

Figure 12 External and Tower relative humidity

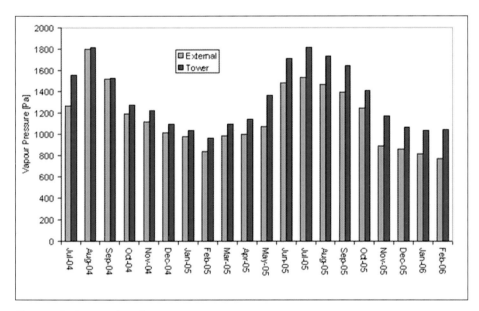

Figure 13 External and Tower vapour pressure

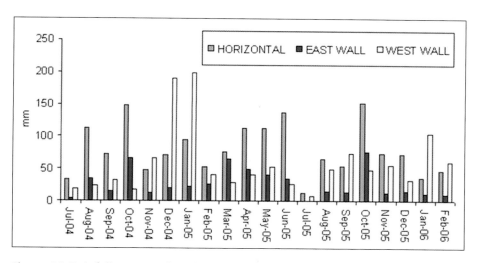

Figure 14 Rainfall measured on the horizontal and at the surface of the east and west walls

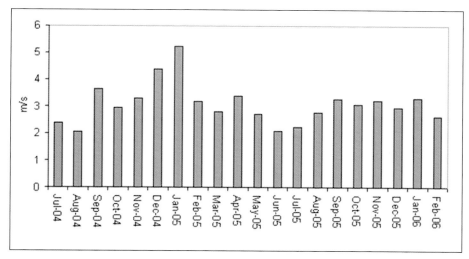

Figure 15 Wind speed

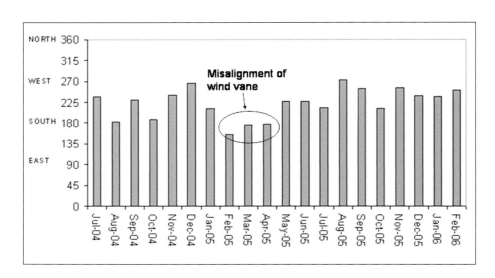

Figure 16 Wind direction

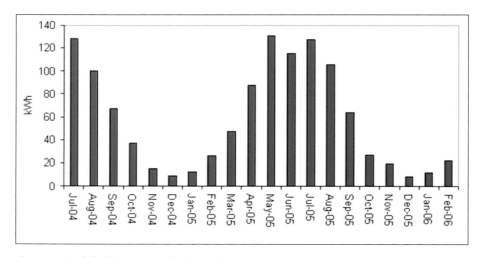

Figure 17 Global horizontal solar radiation

Generally, the climate at Brodick is typical of the west of Scotland: relatively mild and wet. For 2005, the average temperature was 9.8°C, with winter and summer average temperatures of 6.3°C and 14.0°C, respectively. The annual rainfall for 2005 was 1016mm, with similar winter and summer totals of 219mm and 215mm, respectively.

The main wind direction is from the south west (note that, following a visit to Brodick in April 2005, it was observed that the wind vane was misaligned probably as a result of a period of high winds in January 2005 – see Figure 16). The west wall receives about twice as much rainfall as the east wall (Figure 14).

The Tower

Figures 11–13 compare the conditions within the Tower with the external environment.

The internal wall surface and ambient conditions within the Tower are compared in Figures 18–20. Note that due to a data logger fault, data for most of the period November 2004 to January 2005 are missing for the surface conditions.

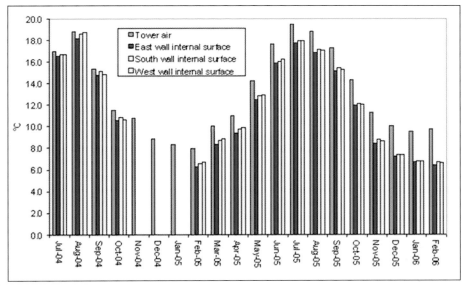

Figure 18 Temperatures at internal surfaces of south, east and west walls compared with ambient

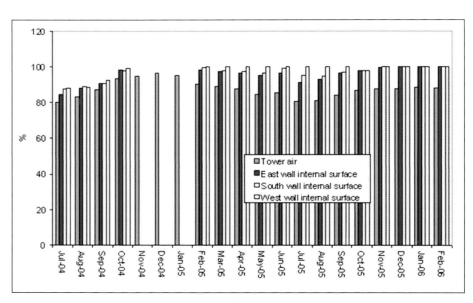

Figure 19 Relative humidities at internal surfaces of south, east and west walls compared with ambient

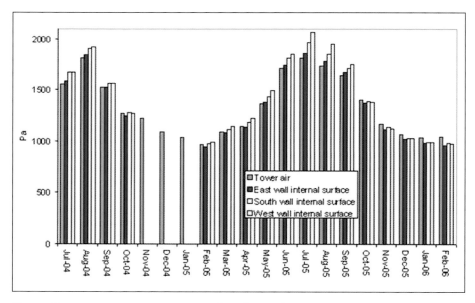

Figure 20 Vapour pressure at internal surfaces of south, east and west walls compared with ambient

Whilst the conditions in the Tower tend to follow the external climate, the Tower tends to dampen the fluctuations. Prior to partitioning, the air temperature in the Tower was an average 1.6K above external and the vapour pressure difference between the Tower and outside was 104Pa (equivalent to an air moisture content of 0.7g/m^3). After partitioning both the Tower temperature and vapour pressure increased compared to the external conditions, with a temperature difference of 4K and a vapour pressure difference of 248Pa (1.7g/m^3). Figure 21 shows the relationship between wind speed (w) and the internal-external temperature difference (DT): the daily average wind speeds have been "binned" and averaged between 0-1m/s, 1-2m/s, 2-3m/s, etc. and the corresponding DT calculated. Similarly, Figure 22 presents the influence of wind speed on the vapour pressure difference (ΔVP). Solar radiation also has an influence on the temperature difference (Figure 23).

The correlations between wind speed and the temperature and vapour pressure differences are stronger before partitioning, similarly between solar radiation and temperature difference. In order to assess the combined influences of both wind and solar radiation, a multiple linear regression analysis was carried out with temperature difference as the dependent variable and wind speed and solar radiation as independent variables. The results are shown in Figure 24 as the predicted (from the regression analysis) and measured values of the temperature difference plotted against both wind speed and solar radiation. Before partitioning the correlation for the relationship is high ($r^2 = 0.995$), but is reduced after the partitioning is in place ($r^2 = 0.808$). Therefore before partitioning, most of the variation in the temperature difference can be explained by the wind speed and solar radiation. However after partitioning, about 20% of the variation is unexplained.

A similar analysis was carried out for the vapour pressure difference between inside the Tower and external conditions (Figure 25). Before partitioning the correlation for the relationship is high ($r^2 = 0.920$), but is considerably reduced after the partitioning is in place ($r^2 = 0.546$), i.e. about 45% of the variation in the vapour pressure difference is unaccounted for by wind and solar.

Before partitioning the Tower conditions tend to converge with the external conditions due to high ventilation rates. After partitioning, other factors are likely to become increasingly significant as the ventilation rate in the Tower decreases; for example the influence of heat and moisture transfer from the occupied rooms below the Tower and moisture penetration through the walls resulting in higher temperatures and vapour pressures.

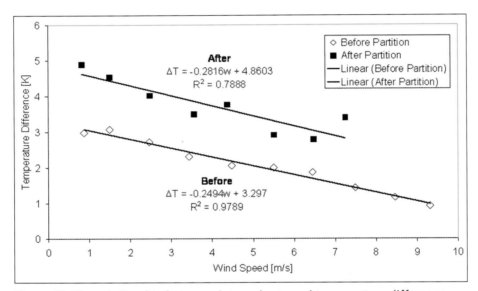

Figure 21 The relationship between internal-external temperature difference and wind speed before and after partitioning

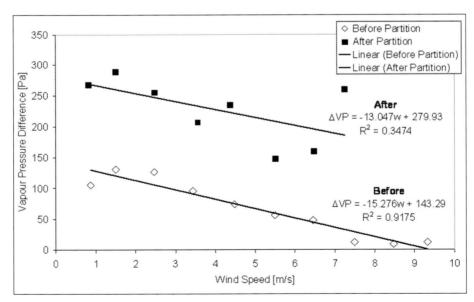

Figure 22 The relationship between internal-external vapour pressure difference and wind speed before and after partitioning

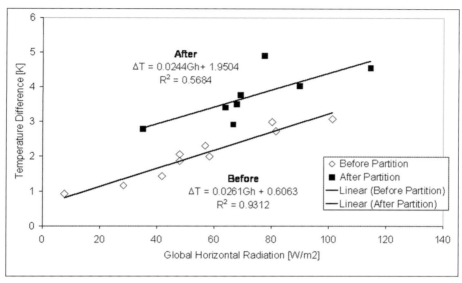

Figure 23 The relationship between internal-external temperature difference and solar radiation before and after partitioning

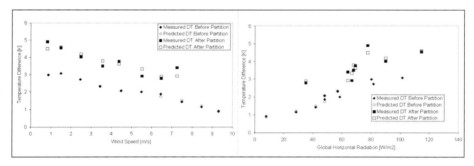

Figure 24 Predictions of temperature difference as a function of both wind speed and solar radiation using multiple linear regression analysis

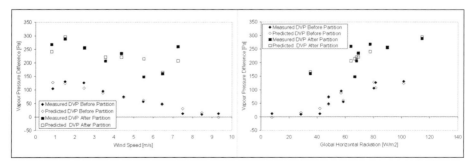

Figure 25 Predictions of vapour pressure difference as a function of both wind speed and solar radiation using multiple linear regression analysis

Partitioning results in an increase in the Tower air temperature compared to the interior wall surfaces (Figure 18): before partitioning the temperature difference is 0.9K and after 2.4K for the average of the three surface measurement locations. However, there is a seasonal effect, with the temperature difference increasing in the winter and decreasing in the summer, which overlays this trend. Figure 26 shows the monthly averages of the Tower air, wall internal surface, wall external surface and external ambient temperatures with solar radiation. The walls warm up relative to the external temperature as solar radiation levels increase from February 2005 and reach a peak temperature in July. The walls then begin to cool as solar radiation levels fall and the wall temperatures converge with the external temperature over autumn and winter.

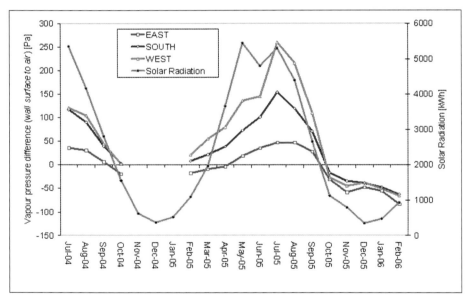

Figure 26 Comparison of Tower air, wall surface and external temperatures with solar radiation. The internal wall surface temperature is the average of the three measurement location, whilst the external surface temperature is that measured on the south wall, where the sensor gives the most reliable readings

The wall surfaces are at a significantly higher relative humidity than the Tower air throughout the monitoring (Figure 19). During the summer of 2005 the east and south walls show decreases in relative humidity in response to the temperature rise (Figure 26). However, the west wall is at or near 100% RH from October 2004, which implies a more or less continuous supply of moisture to the surface. All locations reach saturation during the autumn of 2005.

Whilst the average vapour pressure difference between the wall surface and the room is small (~30Pa) and does not appear to be influenced by partitioning (Figure 20), there are large seasonal fluctuations which depend on wall orientation and solar radiation (Figure 27). Figures 26 and 27 suggests that the wall surface vapour pressures increase relative to the room as the walls warm up and then fall as solar radiation levels and wall temperature fall. The change in vapour pressure at the west wall surface is greatest as it remains at or near saturation for most of the monitoring period.

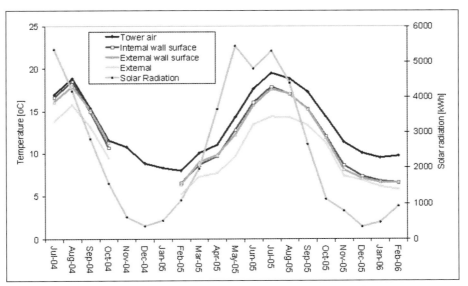

Figure 27 Vapour pressure difference between wall internal surface and Tower air compared with solar radiation

The dowel moisture contents near the inside surface of the walls reflect the above behaviour (Figures 28–30). The dowels in the west wall in particular reach the maximum moisture content (30%) in all three profiles after November 2004, and perhaps more conclusively the discolouration of the wall due to algae has spread (Figure 31). From laboratory investigations carried out by Glasgow Caledonian University it is estimated that, at equilibrium, the dowel moisture content of 30% corresponds to a sandstone moisture content of about 7% by weight (note that the equilibrium moisture content of the sandstone at 90% RH, measured in an absorption isotherm test at 10°C, was 0.6% by weight).

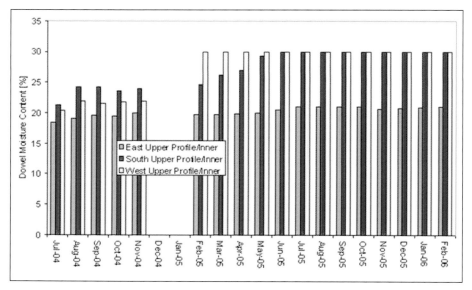

Figure 28 Dowel moisture contents upper profile near inside surface of wall

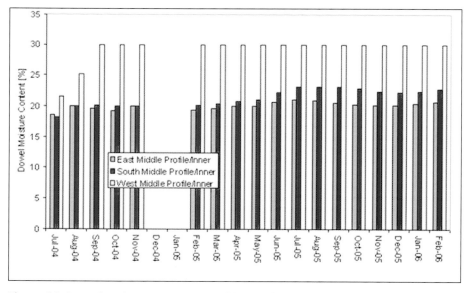

Figure 29 Dowel moisture contents middle profile near inside surface of wall

By the end of the monitoring period it was evident that the three walls were getting wetter, particularly below the gutter level. The dowel moisture content measured toward the outside of the wall (Figure 32) give a similar indication.

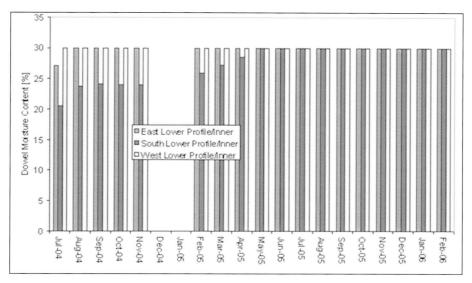

Figure 30 Dowel moisture contents lower profile near inside surface of wall

Figure 31 Spread of algae on west wall: (left) July 2004; (right) May 2006

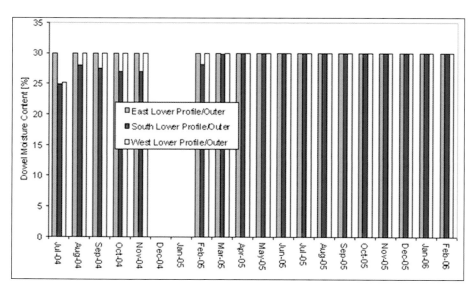

Figure 32 Dowel moisture contents lower profile towards the outside of wall

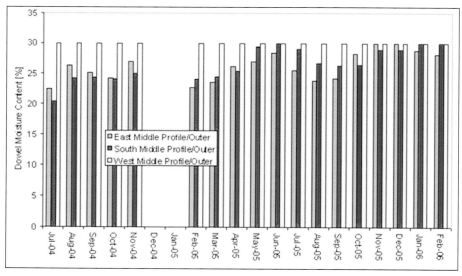

Figure 33 Dowel moisture contents middle profile towards the outside of wall

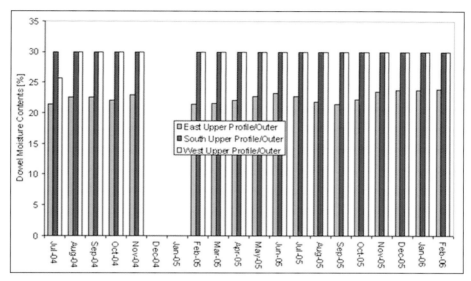

Figure 34 Dowel moisture contents upper profile towards the outside of wall

The dowels towards the outside of the walls in the middle profile (Figure 33) indicate some seasonal drying apart from the west wall. In the upper profiles, only the location in the east wall shows drier conditions (Figure 34).

Whilst the higher rainfall (Figure 14) may exacerbate the problems of the west wall, possible damage to the guttering near to the south-west corner may be the main contributory factor. Additionally, all dowel locations below the gutter level show maximum moisture content. The dowel moisture contents in the locations higher up the walls may correspond to different degrees of exposure of the walls: the main weather direction is from the south-west whilst the east wall receives about half the rainfall falling on the west wall.

Conclusions

Comprehensive measurements were made of the local weather, the environment in the Tower and the condition of the Tower walls. During the monitoring an air barrier was installed to partition off the main room of the Tower in order to reduce ventilation.

The environmental conditions within the unheated Tower respond to changes in the external climate. Prior to partitioning the differences between the Tower and external temperature and vapour pressure are strongly correlated with wind speed and solar radiation. However, following partitioning the response of the Tower conditions are less dependent. The temperature and vapour increase relative to external conditions. The average increase in the moisture content of the air post-partitioning is about 40%. This evidence suggests that the higher air exchange rates prior to patitioning tend to reduce the effects of moisture ingress through the Tower walls.

The wall conditions, e.g. the high surface humidities and dowel moisture contents and algae growth on the west wall, indicate that the Tower is still subject to moisture ingress problems. A cause of the continuing problems may be the result of the deterioration of the guttering around the parapet of the Tower. There is also evidence from dowel moisture contents that the wall conditions depend on the degree of exposure to rainfall: the west wall receives about twice the rainfall of the east wall. Additional factors, which may exacerbate the problems, are the general level of maintenance of the mortar joints of the walls and the porous nature of the sandstone.

The results from the Tower suggest that it is important to improve maintenance regimes to mitigate the effects of climate change, particularly increased precipitation and vapour pressure.

3 Evaluation of the use of wooden dowels as a technique for the measurement of the moisture content of masonry

Paul H. Baker,[1] Graham H. Galbraith,[1] R. Craig McLean[2] and David Nicol[2]

[1]Glasgow Caledonian University, [2]University of Strathclyde

Introduction

The electrical resistance measurement of wooden dowel was chosen as the method for measuring the moisture content of walls at Blickling Hall and Brodick Castle, and laboratory test walls at GCU for the Engineering Historic Futures Project. Whilst the use of dowels is a recognised technique for assessing the state of a wall (is the wall becoming wetter or drier?), there are clearly problems in (a) quantifying the moisture content of masonry from the dowel moisture content without suitable calibration and (b) assessing dynamic changes in moisture content, which may result from flood or drying events rather than longer term seasonal changes. A laboratory investigation was carried out to evaluate the response of the dowels to wetting and drying compared to the behaviour of clay brick (Blickling Hall) and sandstone (Brodick Castle). The moisture contents of dowels inserted into masonry samples was compared with the moisture contents of the samples measured directly using X-ray absorption.

Test procedures

The wetting and drying behaviour of a 17th-century clay brick from Blickling Hall, a sample of sandstone from Brodick Castle and a Locharbriggs sandstone block (Figure 1) were measured indirectly using wooden dowels (Figure 2) inserted into holes drilled in the samples. The moisture content of the dowels was measured at hourly intervals with a Protimeter logger. Direct measurements of the moisture content of the samples were made using X-ray absorption.

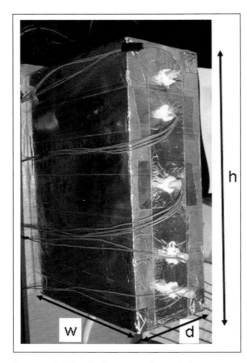

Figure 1 The foil covered sandstone block with wooden dowels inserted

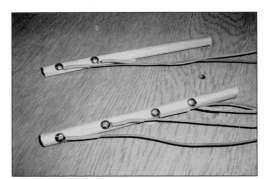

Figure 2 Wooden dowel with electrical connections

Calculation of moisture content from X-ray absorption measurements

The absorption of a transmitted X-ray beam of intensity I follow the Beer-Lambert's law:

$$I = I_o \cdot e^{-\mu\rho x} \qquad (1)$$

where:
μ is the mass attenuation coefficient
ρ is the density of the medium
x is the thickness of the sample
I and I_0 are respectively the transmitted and incident X-ray intensity

For a composite material of i components

$$\ln\frac{I_o}{I} = \sum_i \mu_i \rho_i x_i \qquad (2)$$

The adaptation of Equation 2 to yield an expression for the moisture content of an initially dry material sample can be achieved by applying this relation to various possible experimental configurations between the X-ray source and the detector. As described by Bailly et al.[1] this procedure allows the isolation of the various parameters which contribute to the overall absorption process and enables the moisture content to be defined in terms of the dry and wet conditions. Consider a dry sample of material and the same sample after wetting (Figure 3).

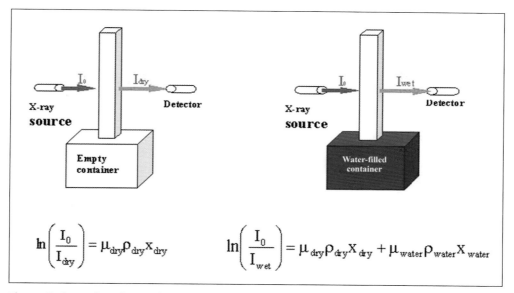

Figure 3 Procedure for moisture content determination

For the dry sample (Figure 3):

$$\ln\left(\frac{I_0}{I_{dry}}\right) = \mu_{dry}\, \rho_{dry}\, X_{dry} \qquad (3)$$

and for the wet sample:

$$\ln\left(\frac{I_0}{I_{wet}}\right) = \mu_{dry}\, \rho_{dry}\, X_{dry} + \mu_{water}\, \rho_{water}\, X_{water} \qquad (4)$$

The moisture content is defined as:

$$u = \frac{m_{water}}{m_{dry}} = \frac{\rho_{water} x_{water}}{\rho_{dry} x_{dry}}$$

(5)

Combining Equations 3, 4 and 5 the moisture content by mass is given by Equation 6:

$$u = \frac{\ln\left(\frac{I_{dry}}{I_{wet}}\right)}{\rho_{dry} x_{dry} \mu_{water}} \qquad [kg/kg]$$

(6)

$$\vartheta = u \frac{\rho_{dry}}{\rho_{water}} \qquad [m^3/m^3]$$

(7)

These relationships assume that the intensity of the incident X-rays is the same for both wet and dry tests.

First test

The Blickling Hall brick and the Brodick Castle sandstone sample were prepared by cutting with a diamond saw to obtain parallel sided samples. A hole was drilled part-way into each sample for the dowel insert. The samples were then dried, the vertical four faces covered with aluminium foil, the dowel inserted and sealed in with silicone sealant (Figure 4).

The samples were placed in a container within the chamber of the X-ray absorption apparatus. The base of each sample was located on supports to raise the sample above the base of the container, in order to allow complete contact between the sample base and water in a water uptake test.

The dowels were connected to a prototype Protimeter data logger.

Dry scans were carried out across each sample at the height of the dowel to determine I_{dry}.

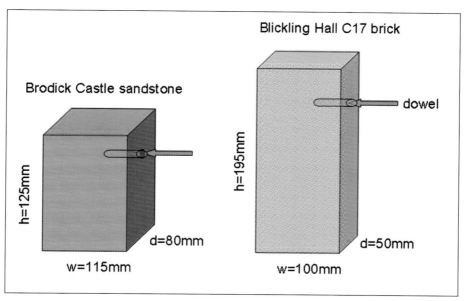

Figure 4 Dimensions and location of dowels of the Brodick Castle sandstone and
Blickling Hall clay brick

Water was then introduced into the container and the water level maintained just
above the base of the samples.

The dowel and sample moisture contents were monitored/measured until both
had reached what was considered an "equilibrium" value, i.e. no further change.
In the case of the Protimeter readings, although the manufacturer states that the
maximum reading is 28.5%, the logger recorded readings up to ~40%.

The samples were then allowed to dry in the chamber. Similarly to the wetting
stage, the dowel and sample moisture contents were monitored/measured until
both were considered "dry", i.e. ~0% for the masonry sample and 13% for the
dowel (the lower limit of the Protimeter). Note that, since the Protimeter logger
would usually be used for measuring timber in buildings, any reading above
~25% would be cause for concern and readings below ~13% would indicate
conditions more likely to be associated with internal joinery or wooden furniture.

Second test

The Locharbriggs sandstone block dimensions were nominally 100mm (d) x 215mm (w) x 300mm (h). The block had been delivered on a polythene covered pallet and was considered to be in a damp condition. Holes were drilled into a face of the block at five locations. The depth of the holes was about 100mm. The drillings were collected, weighed and dried. The estimate of the initial moisture content was 6% by weight (14% by volume). Aluminium foil tape was used to cover all but the top surface of the block (Figure 1). Wooden dowels, with stainless steel screw terminals and cables for connection to data logger, were inserted into the block at the five locations and sealed in with silicone sealant. The dowels were connected to a Protimeter timber moisture content logger, set to record at hourly intervals.

The block was then located in the chamber of the X-ray apparatus (Figure 5). Scans were made across the half of the block to the left of the dowel at each of the five locations (Figure 6). Ventilation of the chamber by provided by an extract fan. The chamber temperature was about 25°C.

Figure 5 Sample located in X-ray chamber

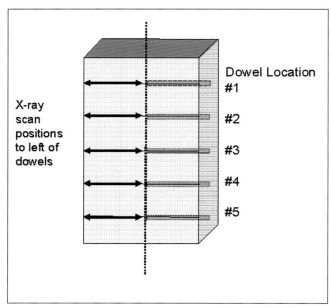

Figure 6 Schematic diagram of scanning positions across block

In our case, the dry intensity, Idry, at each scan location is unknown, since we have started with a wet sample with an unknown moisture distribution, with respect to the dry state. However, taking the initial intensity, Iwet0, as the reference value the change in moisture content may be estimated as follows:

$$u = \frac{\ln\left(\dfrac{I_{wet0}}{I_{wet}}\right)}{\rho_{dry}\, x_{dry}\, \mu_{water}} \qquad \text{[kg/kg]} \qquad (8)$$

Results

First test

The results of the tests on the brick and sandstone are shown in Figures 7 and 8.

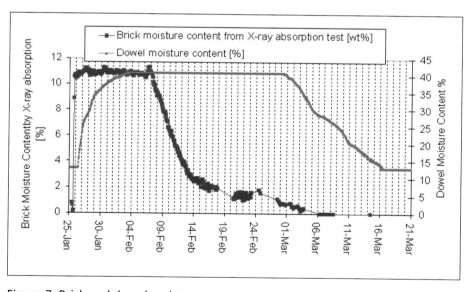

Figure 7 Brick and dowel moisture contents

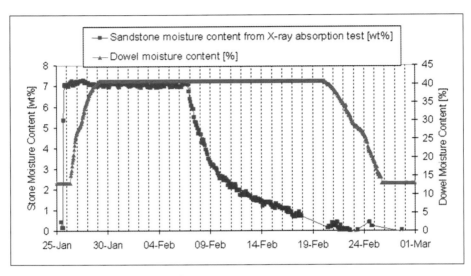

Figure 8 Sandstone and dowel moisture contents

Both the brick and sandstone show rapid water uptake, with the moisture content adjacent to the dowel reaching a steady value within 24 hours. Drying in both cases takes a period of a few weeks. The dowels on the other hand take about four days, in the case of the sandstone, and about nine days for the brick to reach a maximum value during water uptake. During drying, the dowel do not begin to show any decrease in moisture content until the masonry samples are more or less dry (~1% by wt). The rate of drying is particularly slow in the case of the dowel in the brick sample.

Second test

The results of the X-ray absorption tests are shown in Figure 9.

The results show that drying is slow: after four months the moisture content at location #1, nearest the exposed surface, has dried to about the original moisture content as determined by drilling. The drying rate decreases at locations further away from the exposed surface. For comparison the Protimeter measurements of the dowel moisture contents are shown in Figure 10.

Whilst all the dowel measurements increase over the first few days of the test

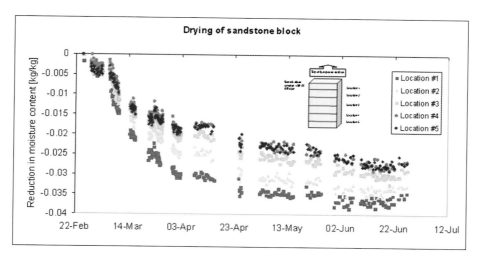

Figure 9 Reduction in moisture content estimated from X-ray scan results of the
five locations

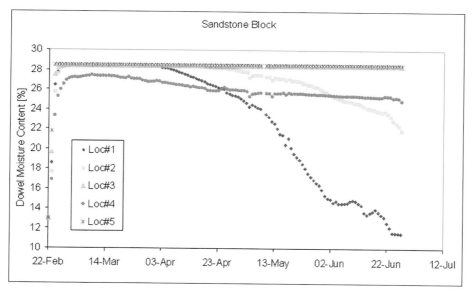

Figure 10 Dowel moisture contents measured using Protimeter data logger.
Note that the upper limit is 28.5%.

indicating a high moisture content, the high readings persist despite the actual
drying of the sample. Only in the case of the dowels at locations #1 and #2, does
the dowel moisture content start to decrease significantly, when the sandstone
moisture content has reduced by about 3% by weight. The shape of the drying
curves for the dowels is also different from that of the sandstone.

Conclusions

The use of dowels is unsatisfactory for dynamic measurements of the moisture content of brick and sandstone in so far as the response lags behind that of the masonry materials, particularly during drying. This may give rise to a pessimistic assessment of the drying stage. However, the dowel measurements may be considered as a reasonable indicator of the state of the masonry over the longer term:

- dowels can indicate that wetting or drying is occurring
- a high dowel moisture content is an indicator of capillary saturation of the masonry.

The difference in behaviour of the dowel in the brick compared to that in the sandstone may be due to the differences in the porosities of the two materials: the moisture capacity of the brick is higher than that of the sandstone.

Reference

1   D.Bailly, M.Campbell, N.Poffa, J.Sun, G.H. Galbraith, R.C. Mclean, C.H. Sanders & G.G. Nielsen, *Moisture transport studies in building materials. Proceedings of Institute of Physics Conference: Sensors and their Applications XII*, Limerick, pp551–557, ISBN 0750309784, September 2003.

4 Investigation of wetting and drying behaviour of replica historic wall constructions

Paul H. Baker,[1] Chris Sanders,[1] Graham H. Galbraith[1] and R. Craig McLean[2]

[1]Glasgow Caledonian University, [2]Strathclyde University

Introduction

Whilst the monitoring of Blickling Hall and Brodick Castle, the case study buildings for the Engineering Historic Futures Project, was essential to improve our understanding of the performance of historic buildings under real climate conditions, there are restrictions to what can be done to the building fabric and environmental conditions for the purposes of measurement and examining drying scenarios. On the other hand, the investigation of suitable test walls in a controlled laboratory environment has advantages which can overcome these drawbacks.

Two test walls were constructed at Glasgow Caledonian University to reflect the wall types at Blickling Hall (brick) and Brodick Castle (sandstone) and be representative of typical historic building walls. The walls have the following benefits:

- The moisture distributions within the walls may be observed under different ambient interior and exterior conditions;
- The walls and boundary conditions are well defined for model validation;
- Sampling and measurement of the walls is unhampered by the need to preserve the historic fabric as completely as possible;
- They allow the testing, to destruction if necessary, of different approaches to drying.

The walls were constructed during the summer of 2004. Whilst instrumentation was installed and monitoring of the walls commenced in December 2004, due to the long curing of the lime mortars used, the first tests were carried out in October 2005 after the walls were considered to have reached a stable condition. The tests involved flooding of the base of the brick wall and spraying of the stone walls followed by a period of unassisted drying. A second flooding test was performed during December 2005 with subsequent forced drying using a de-humidifier. Further spraying of the stone wall was also carried out.

This paper summarises the laboratory investigations carried out for the Engineering Historic Futures Project.

The walls

The materials and wall thicknesses for the constructions were chosen to match as closely as possible those at the two monitoring sites. The walls were constructed on a platform between the two chambers of the environmental chamber at Glasgow Caledonian University. The temperature and relative humidity can be controlled to maintain different conditions in each chamber, corresponding to room conditions (the "warm" chamber) and external conditions (the "cold" chamber). During the construction phase until April 2005 both chambers were maintained at room temperature to aid curing of the mortar. Thereafter, a partition was constructed to separate the two chambers and different conditions were set each side of the walls.

Brick wall
The wall was constructed from a clay replica brick manufactured by traditional methods and a lime mortar (Figures 1 and 2). The wall thickness was approxi-

Figure 1 Side view of brick wall

Figure 2 Warm face of brick wall

mately 650mm. The construction consists of inner and outer leaves with alternate courses of stretcher and header bonds, with a "rubble" fill of half-bricks and mortar.

Stone wall

The wall was construcuted from Locharbriggs sandstone, a lime mortar and a lime putty to create an ashlar finish on the exterior (cold chamber) surface of the wall (Figure 3).

Figure 3 Ashlar finish on cold face of stone wall

Figure 4 Warm face of stone wall

Figure 5 Side view of stone wall

The wall finish is irregular on the warm chamber side (Figure 4) and a rubble fill was used in the core of the wall (Figure 5). The wall is approximately 550mm thick.

Both walls were built on to a semi-rigid plastic sheet with the first layer of brick or stone glued to the sheet with a polyurethane adhesive in order to prevent water penetration at the interface between the base of the wall and the sheet. However, later observations during the course of the flooding tests showed that this was unsuccessful in the case of the brick wall. It was also specified that the walls should be constructed without voids in order to avoid unknown pathways for liquid water transport.

During and for a period of a few weeks after construction, the walls were regularly sprayed with water and covered with damp sacking to promote curing of the lime mortar. In the case of the brick wall, shrinkage cracks were noted in the visible mortar joints and the decision was made to dismantle and rebuild the wall due to the risk that shrinkage cracks may be present in the body of the wall. It was indeed the case that internal cracks were found and testing of the mortar revealed poor carbonation. The most likely cause of the shrinkage was the high suction of the bricks resulting in dehydration of the mortar.[1] Additionally, it was probable that only partial hydration of the hydraulic lime would have occurred throughout the wall. The warm and dry conditions in the laboratory would also exacerbate these problems. After re-building the wall a more careful regime was followed to promote hydration and carbonation by maintaining recommended temperature and humidity levels.

Material properties

Measurements of the main moisture properties of the brick and stone were made. These are summarised in Table 1.

The water absorption coefficient of a sample of Jacobean brick was also measured: 12 kg/(m²h$^{0.5}$), which is about half that of the replica brick. The permeabilities

Table 1 Brick and stone properties					
	Water vapour permeability Wet Cup BS EN ISO 12572 [kg/(m.s.Pa)]	Water vapour permeability Dry Cup BS EN ISO 12572 [kg/(m.s.Pa)]	Water absorption coefficient EN ISO14148 [kg/(m²h$^{0.5}$)]	Capillary moisture content [wt%]	Bulk density [kg/m³]
Replica Brick	1.42E-11 (s.d.±18%)	1.38E-11 (s.d.±15%)	26.2	11.9	1712 1712
Sandstone	1.37E-11 (s.d.±3%)	1.73E-11 (s.d.±5%)	23.9	9.0	1905 (s.d.±2%)
s.d. standard deviation, where more than one sample tested.					

of the replica brick show significant variation, which reflect the variability in the degree of firing of the samples used for the permeability tests.

The sorption isotherms of the brick and stone samples were also measured at 10, 20 and 30°C (Figures 6 and 7). The Figures represent the equilibrium moisture

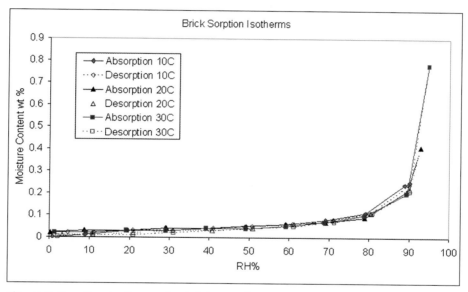

Figure 6 Sorption isotherms for brick sample

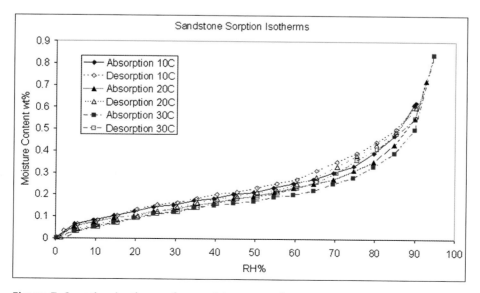

Figure 7 Sorption isotherms for sandstone sample

content for the range of relative humidities between 0–95% for absorption and desorption.

Generally, in the hygroscopic region (below <98% relative humidity) the brick and stone samples have a low moisture content <1% by weight. Whilst the properties of the mortar were not generally measured due to the difficulties in producing satisfactory samples which were crack free and of suitable dimensions, the sorption isotherm of a sample of the mortar used in the construction of the sandstone walls was measured (Figure 8). This shows higher moisture contents over the range of relative humidities. The negative value obtained at 0% relative humidity during desorption may indicate the loss of chemically bound moisture.

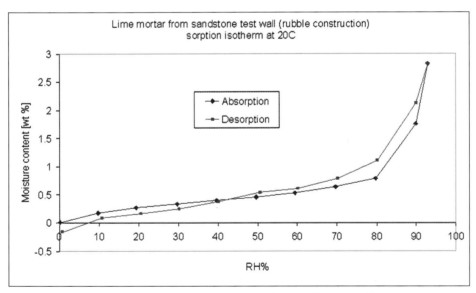

Figure 8 Sorption isotherm of lime mortar used in sandstone wall

Instrumentation of the walls

The instrumentation of the walls was carried out in December 2004. A semi-rigid plastic sheeted was glued using polyurethane adhesive to the side of each wall as a moisture barrier. A pre-drilled chipboard template was then glued to the plastic (Figure 9). 12mm diameter holes were then drilled into the side of the wall to a

depth of about 500mm, i.e. half-way into the wall, and the side of the wall
finished off with a sheet of insulation. A sensor assembly was inserted into each of
the holes (Figure 10).

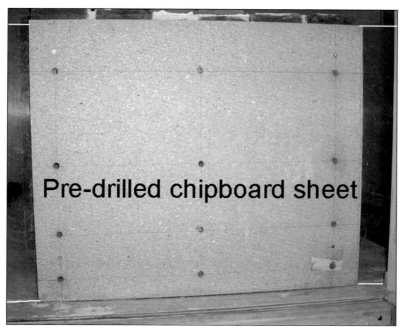

Figure 9 Template for drilling holes for sensors

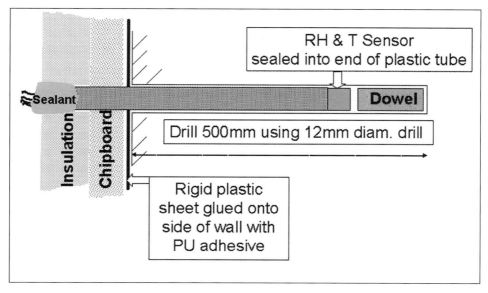

Figure 10 Sensors assembly inserted into wall

The assembly consisted of a combined temperature and humidity sensor and a wooden dowel for measuring moisture content. Stainless steel screws were inserted through cable terminals at each end of the dowel. Heat-shrink sleeving was shrunk around each end of the dowel and used as former for a resin compound in order to provide a protective seal for the terminal assembly. The humidity sensors were chosen for their small size, resistance to contaminants, stability and accuracy (±2% relative humidity). The sensors are able to recover from the presence of liquid water. The sensor response shows some hysteresis above 90% relative humidity. Taking this into account, the estimated uncertainty in the relative humidity measurements above 90% is ±5%.

The sensor locations are shown in Figure 11 and the location codes in Figure 12.

The temperature and humidity sensors were connected to an Agilent 34970A data acquisition system and logged at 5 minute intervals. Chamber temperatures and relative humidities were also measured. The dowel moisture contents were measured using Protimeter Humilogger data loggers at either hourly or at four hour intervals.

Sufficient material was obtained from the walls by drilling the estimate the moisture content of the vertical profiles in each wall (Table 2).

Table 2 Moisture content (wt%) of the walls obtained by drilling

	Profile 1	Profile 2	Profile 3
Brick	1.4	3.3	1.7
Sandstone	0.5	7.1	2.1

The estimates indicate that the cores of both walls, particularly the sandstone, have remained wet since construction.

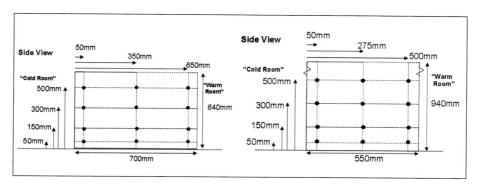

Figure 11 Sensor locations: (left) brick wall; (right) stone wall

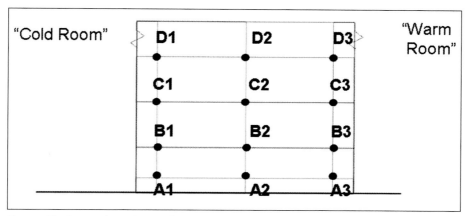

Figure 12 Sensor location codes

Conditioning of the walls

Following instrumentation the conditions in both chambers were maintained at nominally 20°C and 60% relative humidity. An insulated partition was built above the walls to separate the two chambers in April 2005. The conditions in the cold chamber were re-set to maintain nominally 10°C and 85% relative humidity, however the conditions in both chambers deviated from the set points over time due to problems with the air conditioning plant (Figure 13).

Figures 14 and 15 show the temperatures and relative humidities measured in the core of the walls (vertical profile 2) during the period December 2004 to September 2005.

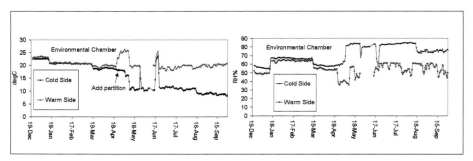

Figure 13 Environmental chamber conditions: (left) temperatures; (right) relative humidity

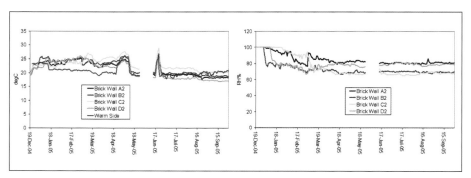

Figure 14 Brick wall core temperatures (left) and relative humidities (right)

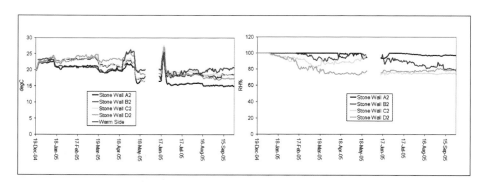

Figure 15 Stone wall core temperatures (left) and relative humidities (right)

Generally before partitioning of the chamber, locations in the walls show higher temperatures than the chamber conditions (Figures 14 and 15). This is likely to be a consequence of the evolution of heat during the mortar curing process. The relative humidities decrease over time from their initial 100% levels (liquid present). The initial rate of decrease is relatively steep for brick and thereafter reduces (Figure 14). The process is slower for the sandstone and the relative humidities are still high (~98%) in location A2 in September 2005 (Figure 15). These observations are reflected to some extent by the dowel moisture contents (Figure 16 and 17), although small scale laboratory tests[2] indicate that the moisture content of the brick or stone needs to fall below a critical level before the dowel responds, due to the suction of the timber relative to that of the brick or stone. The dowel measurements are not considered further in this report due their poor response to transient events.

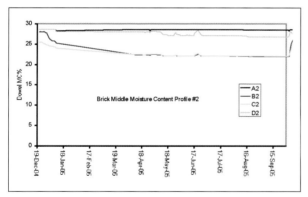

Figure 16 Dowel moisture contents in the vertical profile 2 of the brick wall

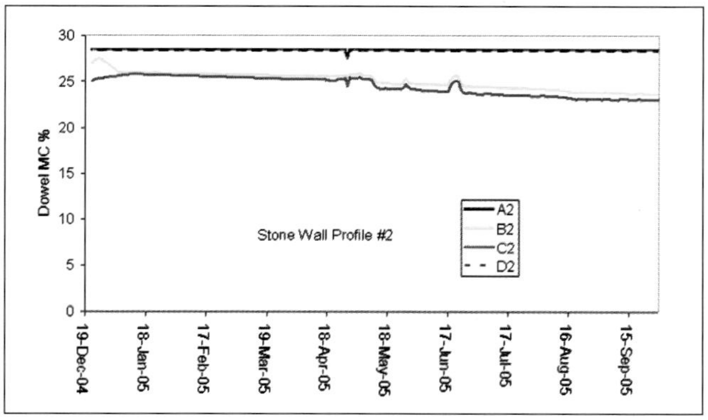

Figure 17 Dowel moisture contents in the vertical profile 2 of the sandstone wall

During September 2005, the conditions within the walls were considered to be close enough to equilibrium to investigate wetting and drying performance of the walls.

A reservoir was built at the base of each wall in the cold chamber (Figure 18) to facilitate the tests.

Figure 18 Cold side of stone wall showing reservoir

Flooding of brick wall October 2005

The brick wall was subjected to flooding from the cold side. A water level of about 100mm was maintained for a period of three days between 4 and 6 October 2005 (Figure 19). It was estimated that the wall absorbed about 50 litres of water. It was observed that water penetrated through to the warm side of the wall, probably via the interface between the plastic sheet and the base of the wall. On the cold side, water rose up to the first mortar joint above the level of the flood water. Damp was apparent in only the first course of bricks, up to the first mortar joint on the warm side.

The wall was allowed to dry out without intervention until a second flooding test carried out at the end of November 2005.

Figure 19 Flooding of brick wall

Flooding of brick wall November 2005

The second flood was carried out between 25 November and 1 December 2005. 100 litres of water were used and the water level initially covered the first three courses of brick on the cold side of the wall. By 1 December enough water remained to cover the first course of bricks. This was removed prior to drying using a de-humidifier on the warm side of the wall. Water had penetrated underneath the wall. It was evident that there was evidence of damp in the lower four courses of bricks (Figure 20).

The de-humidification set-up is shown in Figures 21 and 22. Polythene sheet was loosely fixed to cover the brick wall and allow ventilation at the top edge. The sheet was fixed at the sides and base of the wall. The de-humidifier hose was fitted under the sheet. Additional temperature and relative humidity sensors were installed to measure the conditions within the enclosure.

The de-humidifier was allowed to operate until 29 March 2006. The enclosure was then removed. The average conditions in the enclosure over the operation period were 26°C and 24% relative humidity, compared with 20°C and 50% for the warm chamber (Figure 23), however there was a failure in the control of the environmental chamber during the first few days of de-humidification.

Figure 20 Warm side of brick wall showing penetration of water and evidence of damp after flooding (1 December 2005)

Figure 21 Polythene enclosure covering warm side of brick wall

Figure 22 Dessicant wheel de-humidifier connected to enclosure by flexible hose

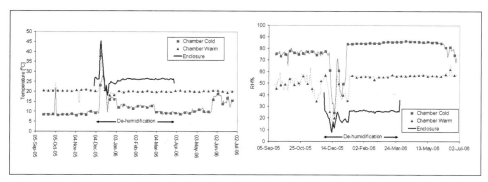

Figure 23 Environmental chamber conditions from September 2005:
(left) temperatures; (right) relative humidities

Flooding tests results and discussion

The relative humidities in the wall measured from September 2005, prior to the
first flood, are shown in Figures 24–26.

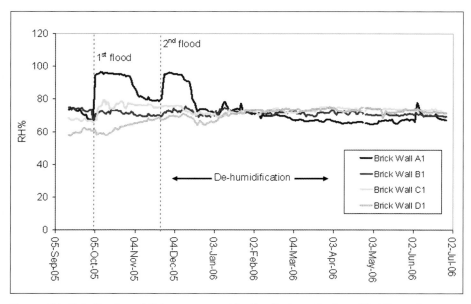

Figure 24 Relative humidities measured in the first vertical profile 50mm from
cold surface of the brick wall

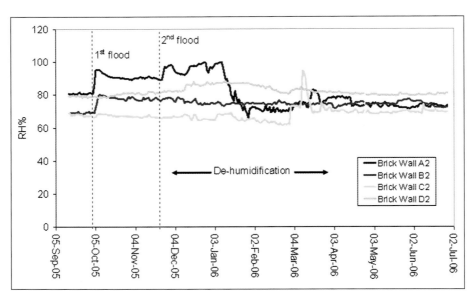

Figure 25 Relative humidities measured in the second vertical profile in the core of the brick wall

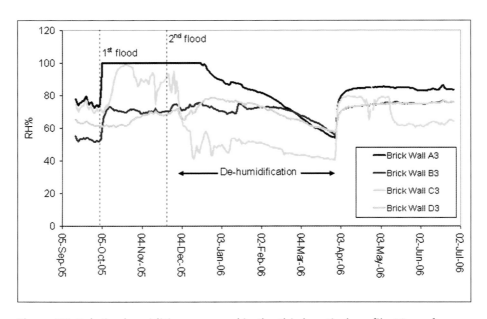

Figure 26 Relative humidities measured in the third vertical profile 50mm from warm surface of the brick wall

First flood event

The effect of flooding on the cold side of the wall is most evident at the lowest measurement position (A1), although the humidities further up the wall (C1 & D1) increase after the first flood event (Figure 24) as moisture redistributes. The relative humidity at A1 begins to decrease rapidly from 31 October until 8 November, when the rate slows.

In the core of the wall (Figure 25) the relative humidities at locations A2 and B2 rise sharply, then reduce more slowly.

The effect of the flooding is most apparent near the warm side of the wall (Figure 26). The relative humidity at location A3 rises to and remains at 100% until during the de-humidification stage. The relative humidities at B3 and C3 rise sharply, whilst at D3 it increases more gradually. At C3, after reaching 99% on 23rd October, the relative humidity begins to fall. Significant drying at the warm side of the wall is therefore not apparent until after the second flood when de-humidification is applied.

Second flood event

During flooding, the most notable increases in relative humidity are at locations A1 and A2 (Figures 24 and 25). After the start of de-humidification on 1 December, drying out of the wall is most apparent in location A1 near the cold side of the wall. All locations near the cold side reach a similar level of humidity by early January 2006.

In the core of the wall, the relative humidity at location A2 decreases from 8 January until 29 January. Thereafter, the relative humidities measured at the four locations in the core tend to a steady value prior to the end of the de-humidification (Figure 25).

The humidities near the cold side of the wall and at its core appear to be unaffected by the removal of the de-humidifier as wall temperatures fall.

Near the warm side of the wall, the relative humidity at location A3 begins to decrease after 18 December and continues to fall until the end of the de-humidification test converging with the relative humidities at B3 and D3 (Figure 26) to about 60%. After de-humidification, the relative humidities increase to about 75% (B3 & D3) and 85% (A3) as the temperature near to the surface falls due to the removal of the de-humidifier (Figure 27). The behaviour at C3 appears to be anomalous, however after testing it was discovered that part of the brick face had broken away exposing the sensor.

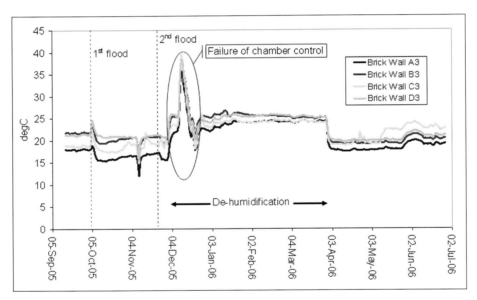

Figure 27 Temperatures measured in the third vertical profile 50mm from warm surface of the brick wall

Spray testing of sandstone wall

During the first flood test, the stone wall was sprayed with water to simulate driving rain (Figure 28). 10 litres of water were applied over a 50 minute period using a hand pumped pressure spray. The surface was then covered with a felt underlay material, which was sprayed with water until damp, in order to keep moisture at the wall surface. The felt was removed after three days.

Further spraying of the wall was carried out on an ad hoc basis during November-

December 2005 and April–May 2006. The amount of water sprayed at the wall during each session was equivalent to typical daily levels of rainfall at Brodick Castle. Measured quantities of water were sprayed onto the wall and estimates of the amount absorbed by the wall were made by collecting and weighing the run-off from the wall. Figure 29 shows the relative humidities through profile D of the wall and the quantities of water absorbed. In Figure 30 the amount of run-off is compared with the amount of water sprayed onto the wall in each session.

The results indicate that whilst the relative humidity near to the cold surface rises in response to the spraying, the conditions within the core of the wall and near to the warm side of the wall appear to be largely unaffected.

Figure 28 Spraying of stone wall

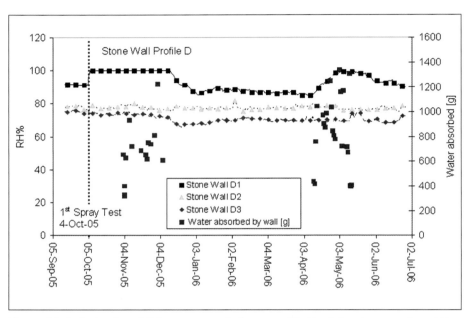

Figure 29 Relative humidities measured along profile D of the stone wall and the quantities of water absorbed during spray testing

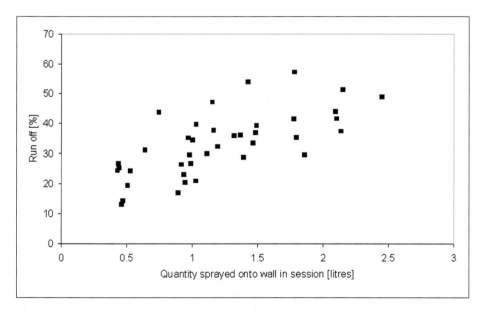

Figure 30 The amount of run-off of water from stone wall surface compared with the total amount of water sprayed onto the wall in one session

The run-off generally increases with the quantity sprayed onto the wall (Figure 30) The rate of spraying, which was not measured, will also influence the run-off: generally the researcher carrying out the spraying aimed to complete the task as quickly as possible regardless of quantity. The rate at which the moisture can be absorbed into the surface of the wall is constrained by the water absorption coefficient of the sandstone.

Summary and conclusions

Two laboratory test walls were constructed in the environmental chamber at Glasgow Caledonian University during the summer of 2004. The walls are representative of the constructions at the two case study sites for the Engineering Historic Futures Project at Blickling Hall (brick and lime mortar) and Brodick castle (sandstone and lime mortar with an ashlar external finish). Different conditions were maintained either side of the walls to simulate indoor and outdoor temperatures and humidities.

The walls were conditioned for over a year to allow the curing of the mortars to progress. It was evident from humidity measurements within the walls that, by September 2005, both walls were approaching an equilibrium condition. However, locations in the core of the sandstone wall still showed high humidities.

Flooding test on the brick wall

Two flooding tests were performed on the brick wall. After the first flooding event, the wall was allowed to dry naturally under the environmental chamber conditions for about 50 days. The second flooding event was followed by a four month period of de-humidification with average boundary conditions of 26°C and 24% relative humidity.

Water uptake in the brick wall was most significant in the lower profile and towards the warm side of the wall due to the penetration of water beneath the base of the wall. The interval between the two flooding events was insufficient to allow drying of the core of the wall and near the warm side under natural conditions. However, drying was apparent near to the cold side at the lowest location after the first flood.

The results of de-humidification show that about 18 days elapse before the relative humidity begins to fall below 100% at the wettest location 50mm above the base, near the warm side of the wall. Drying out at this location was still in progress some 100 days later at the end of the test. The humidities at higher measurement locations show redistribution of moisture over the de-humidification period and converge with the relative humidity at the lower location after about 85 days. Once the de-humidifier is removed, the relative humidities rise from about 60% to 75–85%, due to the lowering of the surface temperature of the wall.

The humidity at the wettest location within the core of the brick wall remains high for a period of 38 days after the start of de-humidification. The humidity then falls and begins to converge with the humidities measured at the other core locations after a further 21 days. Near the cold side of the wall a similar phenomenon occurs: the humidity at the wettest location begins to fall after 10 days and converges with that at the other cold side locations after a further 13 days.

The main conclusions of the de-humidification test are as follows:

- De-humidification promotes the conditions required for drying, however achieving a suitable equilibrium moisture content takes time.
- The core of the brick wall took about two months to dry. The cold side of the wall reached a stable condition after a month. The core and cold side humidities were unaffected by the removal of the de-humidifier.
- Near to the warm side, the wall is still drying out after four months of de-humidification.
- The humidities near to the wall surface rise after removal of the de-humidifier. Whilst the humidity levels may represent moisture contents below 1%, if the surface relative humidities remain high there may be a risk of mould growth.

Whilst it is evident that the drying process requires several months, even using a de-humidifier, time constraints did not allow a proper comparison with natural drying. The 50 day period allowed for the natural drying of the wall was insufficient except for locations near to the cold side of the wall, where the drying time was similar to the de-humidification test.

Spraying of the sandstone wall

The sandstone wall was sprayed regularly with water to simulate driving rain. The results indicate that whilst the relative humidity near to the cold surface rises in response to the spraying, the conditions within the core of the wall and near to the warm side of the wall appear to be largely unaffected. In comparison, the monitoring results from Brodick Castle indicate that moisture ingress in a wall of similar construction and material properties is largely the result of the deterioration of the sealing of guttering chased into the stonework.

The amount of run-off collected from the wall during the spray tests was found to increase with the quantity of water sprayed onto the wall in a session, although the rate of spraying also has an influence. The amount of water absorbed by the wall is limited by its surface absorption characteristics.

The implication is that a well constructed (and a well maintained) wall should perform to keep moisture out of a building under present climatic conditions with the relatively high levels of precipitation experienced at Brodick Castle and with the increased rainfall of the future climate scenario.

References

1   Scottish Lime Centre, "Accelerated Carbonation – Engineering Historic Futures", report produced for Historic Scotland, August 2004.

2   Baker P.H., "Evaluation of the use of wooden dowels as a technique for the measurement of the moisture content of masonry", report circulated to EHF consortium, June 2006.

5 Development and use of computer modelling of historic wall constructions

Nigel Blades,[1] Ian Ridley,[2] Theo Chen[2] and Tadj Oreszczyn[2]

[1]UCL Centre for Sustainable Heritage, [2]Bartlett School of Graduate Studies, UCL

1. Introduction

In the Engineering Historic Futures project it was planned that as part of Task 5 computer modelling techniques would be used to help understand the behaviour of moisture in historic building fabric during the following processes:

i. natural wetting and drying of building walls through the annual climate cycle

ii. climate change and its effect on the current moisture balance of masonry walls and future implications for the conservation and maintenance of such walls

iii. forced drying of building fabric by typical heating and dehumidification methods after flood damage or extreme moisture penetration; implications of these processes for conservation of wall fabric

In order to simulate these processes it was necessary to have a model capable of simulating climate processes, in outdoor and indoor environments, and wall moisture processes; critically, the model needs to couple these two types of process together so that the influence of climate on the building fabric can be assessed.

Models in building simulation aim to predict either: (a) the moisture content of a building fabric such as its walls, (b) the relative humidity and temperature of the adjacent room. There are two different classes of computer simulation software used to examine the above-mentioned hygrothermal environments within buildings. The first consists of building simulation thermal and energy models used to predict energy consumption, air conditioning loads and thermal comfort within buildings. These models often consider the effect of the moisture buffering capacity of the building fabric on the relative humidity and temperature of the air but do not predict moisture profiles within the fabric. EnergyPlus is an example of such software. The second type involve heat, air and moisture (HAM) transfer models. A popular example is the WuFi software. HAM models examine the transfer of moisture through porous building materials and predict profiles of moisture content and temperature within a building element such as a wall, floor or ceiling, when they are exposed to changing boundary conditions of temperature, relative humidity, solar radiation and wind, on the surface of the wall. However, they do not predict the indoor climate of the building constructed of those elements.

For air-conditioned buildings where the internal environment is well controlled, existing models are sufficient to answer most energy or comfort questions relating to the building environment. However in many historic buildings the environment is 'free floating', i.e. it is not controlled, but fluctuates with climate and occupancy. In these cases existing models are not sufficient. This is particularly the case where building fabric can interact with the environment, storing heat and moisture, for instance.

Many existing models are also restricted by the fact that they can often only solve problems in either 1- or 2-dimensions but not both. (A 1-dimensional model simulates heat and moisture properties along a linear profile through the cross-section of a wall whereas a 2-dimensional model can simulate properties in a vertical profile and cross-section).

In order to address these issues, as part of EHF it was decided to develop a new model, *Canute*, that would couple the wall and room domains and be able to simulate fully the processes described in the research aims at the beginning of the introduction. The Canute model provides a strategy for calculating such a system and in the future, gives the backdrop to incorporating HAM algorithms into a building simulation program. The work of model development was two-fold. The first aim was to produce a model that uses a general finite-element package (e.g. COMSOL Multiphysics™) to generate the model mesh, i.e. the cross-sectional representation of the room and walls to be simulated with the nodes, or points at which the model calculates heat and moisture properties. The second development activity was to write the building physics equations of the model in the Matlab Engineering/Mathematics package. The diagram below shows the type of mesh employed in Canute. The mesh represents a vertical cross-section through a building, in this case the Blickling Hall case study room. The density of the mesh reflects the density of points at which the model calculates the wall properties. The rectangles are the building elements and are defined with appropriate physical properties for wall, wall against earth, ceiling and floor.

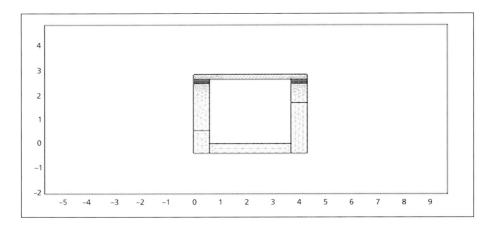

There are two stages to the Canute model: (a) a finite-element time-dependent stage for the moisture-content in the building walls and (b) a calculation of the adjacent room conditions (i.e. relative humidity and temperature). The first stage calculates the moisture-content in the walls as well as the moisture and heat fluxes entering/exiting them. These fluxes are then used to calculate the corresponding relative humidity and temperature in the interior room at the end of the current discretized time domain. Once calculated, the relative humidity and temperature provide the boundary conditions needed to solve the moisture-content in the walls in the next time domain. These steps continue until the final time-step of the model is reached.

The Canute model was constructed over a three-year period. Quite early on in its development case study simulations of the two EHF field test sites at Blickling Hall and Brodick Castle began to be constructed using the developing model, based on project measurements of the building fabric dimensions and materials. Physical properties of the Blickling brick and Brodick stone were determined in the laboratory at Glasgow Caledonian University. Climate data for the outdoor and indoor environment at both sites were measured and used in conjunction with the model according to the following scheme:

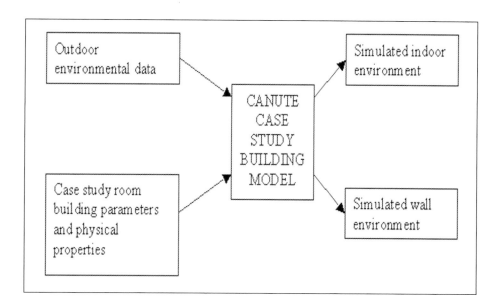

2. Testing of the Canute model against measured data from the case study sites

The simulated indoor climate data were compared with measured indoor climate data for each site to evaluate the model predictions. This was done in an iterative process throughout the project in order to refine and improve the Canute model. Figures 1–4 show the comparison between model predictions and measured data for the indoor environments of the two case study sites, using the most recent version of Canute.

As can be seen from the results in Figures 1 and 2 of the Canute Blickling Hall basement room model, there is very good agreement between the modelled and measured temperature, but less good agreement for the relative humidity, where the measured data show greater fluctuations and frequent saturation of the air which are not simulated by the model. Figures 3 and 4 compare the measured and modelled data in the final version of the Brodick Castle tower room model. Here there is again very good agreement between measured and modelled temperature.

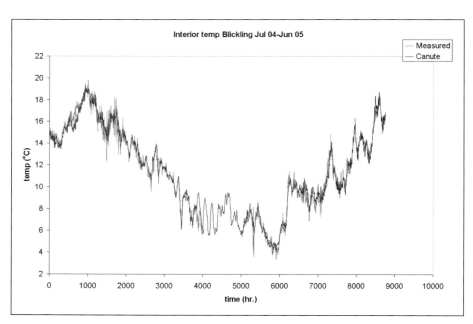

Figure 1 Comparison of Canute modelled and measured temperature for Blickling basement, for a complete annual cycle.

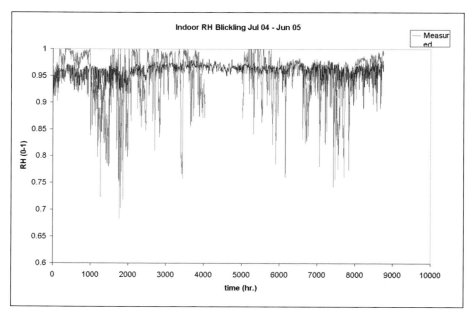

Figure 2 Comparison of Canute modelled and measured relative humidity for Blickling basement, for a complete annual cycle.

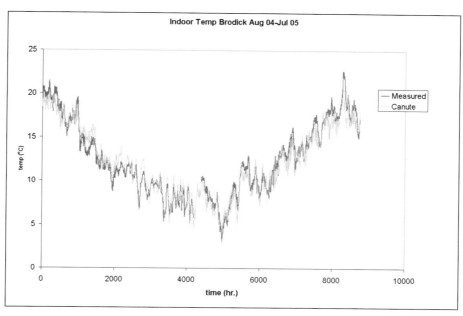

Figure 3 Comparison of Canute modelled and measured temperature for Brodick Castle tower room, for a complete annual cycle.

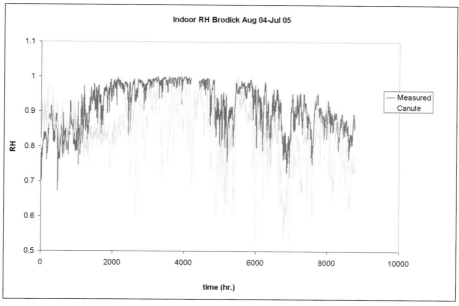

Figure 4 Comparison of Canute modelled and measured relative humidity for Brodick Castle tower room, for a complete annual cycle.

The relative humidity shows less good agreement between measured and modelled data, though at Brodick the simulated data show greater fluctuations than the measured data. This may be related to the high air exchange rate used in the model for this site (7 ach, estimated from pressurisation testing, 2006).

These two case study models suggest that the Canute model is able to simulate indoor temperature quite accurately but is less accurate in its relative humidity simulation, but may be adequate for the purposes of the modelling required in this project, which aims to predict relative changes and is focused on the wall properties rather than effects on the room environment.

The Canute model in its coupled form also simulates the wall heat and moisture conditions. Figures 5–8 below show the simulated wall conditions over one year for the two case study sites.

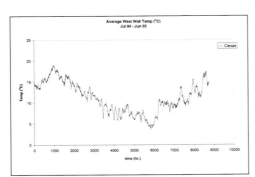 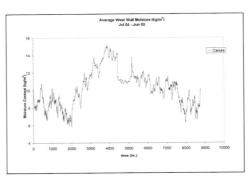

Figures 5 and 6 Simulated wall properties for Blickling Hall basement room over an annual cycle.

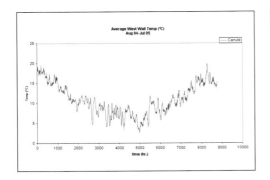 

Figures 7 and 8 Simulated wall properties for Brodick Castle tower room over an annual cycle.

It was originally the intention in the project methodology to test the modelled wall moisture contents against measured data from the wall dowel resistance probes. However, problems experienced with the dowel measurement technique in terms of saturation of probes and long response times meant that ultimately this was not possible.

This reflects a fundamental problem with moisture monitoring in building fabric. New monitoring techniques are being developed by an EPSRC-funded project, which should, in the long-term, solve the problem of time-resolved measurements of building fabric moisture content.

For the present project, an alternative method of testing the Canute model predictions had to be adopted. The approach taken was to compare the Canute model predictions for various test cases, including idealised situations and the Blickling and Brodick case study sites with model predictions from established building simulation programmes. This was done using EnergyPlus (EnergyPlus, 2006) as a comparison for the prediction of the indoor climate based on external climate inputs and simple building properties; and WuFi (WuFi, 2006) to simulate the wall heat and moisture properties. Ongoing testing and validation of EnergyPlus and Wufi is being undertaken by the developers of these respective softwares (EnergyPlus, 2006, Wufi 2006). Canute was also assessed using the HAMSTAD benchmarks (Hagentoft, 1999), which the authors of the HAMSTAD report state "could be used as references for the assessment of existing and new software"

3. Results of Canute model testing against other established air and fabric building simulation models

The predictions of Canute were compared with an established building simulation model, EnergyPlus. The test case was based upon a modelling exercise used by the IEA Annex 41 sub-task (ECBCS, 2006), which is investigating whole building hygrothermal simulation. The relative humidity inside a simple case study building, shown in Figure 9, and the heating load need to maintain an internal temperature of 20°C were calculated.

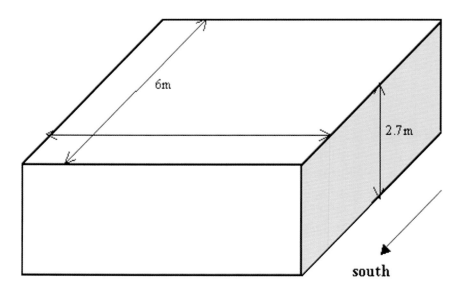

Figure 9 Annex 41 sub-task case study building.

The fabric of the test building, concrete, had the following properties:

(a) Material data

Sorption isotherm:

$\phi = \exp(0.0011 \cdot (1-(w/300)^{-1.99}))$

Vapour diffusion:

$\delta_p = 1.76 \times 10^{-10} \cdot (0.116 + 0.00628 \times \exp(4.19 \times \exp(0.0011 \times (1 - 8510.3/w^{1.99})))) (s)$

Liquid water permeability:

$K = 0 (s)$

Thermal conductivity:

$\lambda = 0.18 \ (W/mK)$

Heat capacity for dry material:

$c_0 = 840 \ (J/kgK)$

Density of dry material:

$\rho_0 = 650 \ (kg/m^3)$

As Canute does not model glass windows, the Annex 41 test case had to be modified, with the windows being removed. Direct comparison with the identical Annex 41 test case and results could not be made.

(b) Heat and Ventilation data

Internal moisture gain = 500 g/h from 9:00–17:00 every day.

Internal heat gain=800 W from 9:00–17:00 every day.

Ventilation = 0.5 ach or 1.389E–4 ac/s.

Indoor temperature: T_{in} = 20°C.

Initial Conditions: $T_{in,0}$ = 20°C, $\phi_{in,0}$ = 0.80.

External surface transfer coefficients:

$\alpha_{c,out}$ = 1/0.034 (W/m²K)

$\beta_{p,out}$ = 1/(1.6 * 10^(7)) (s/m)

Indoor surface transfer coefficients:

$\alpha_{c,in}$ = 1/0.121 (W/m²K)

$\beta_{p,in}$ = 1/(5 * 10^(7)) (s/m)

(c) Weather information

A test weather file from Annex 41 was used:

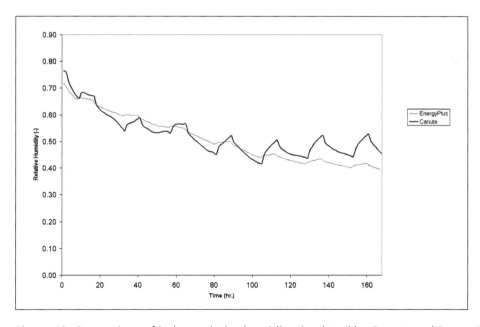

Figure 10 Comparison of indoor relative humidity simulated by Canute and EnergyPlus.

Results

It can be seen, Figure 10, that the Canute model predicts less moisture buffering than EnergyPlus, with greater daily amplitude swings in RH resulting. In comparison with measured data, (Annex 41, 2005) EnergyPlus and been previously found to over damp RH predictions, Canute's performance relative to EnergyPlus was encouraging, whereas the amplitude of the RH swings predicted by EnergyPlus are only 1% RH, Canute predicts swings of 9% RH, (direct comparison with this Annex 41 test case is not possible due to the presence of windows in this Annex case). To further investigate the level of moisture buffering predicted by the Canute model, the predicted RH was compared to the RH predicted by an analytical solution of the model, for another Annex 41 test case. It was found, Figure 11, that the Canute results showed good agreement with the analytical method.

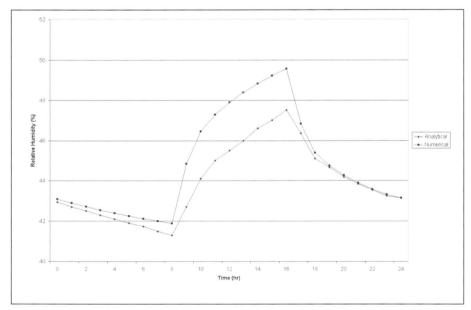

Figure 11 Comparison of RH predicted by Canute, numerically (i.e. solved by model iteration) and solved analytically (i.e. from building physics first principles).

There is good agreement, Figure 12, between the heating loads predicted by the EnergyPlus air model and Canute. Note that Canute models a 2D slice of the test room, and does not model heat flows through the end walls. The test building as modelled in EnergyPlus was modified to also neglect heat flows through the end walls to allow comparison.

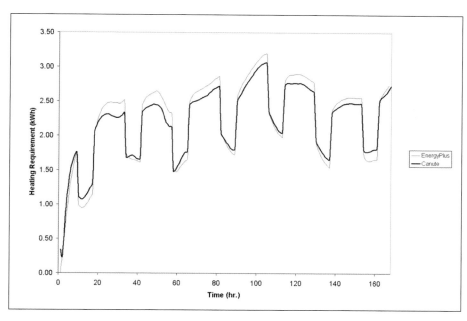

Figure 12 Comparison of Canute and EnergyPlus simulated indoor energy requirements

The predictions of Canute were compared with those of an established Heat and Moisture movement building fabric model Wufi. In this example, a test wall, 600mm thick and 2.5m high, based on a wall at the Blickling case study site, was modelled. The fabric of the test wall had the following properties

(a) Material data
Sorption isotherm:

$\phi = exp(0.012484 - 0.012484 \times (781250/26429963 \times w)^{-1.06279}$

Vapour diffusion:

$\delta_p = 1.42 \times 10^{-11} \, (s)$

Liquid water permeability:

$K = 4.3869 \times 10^{-14} \times w^{2.0628} \, (s)$

Thermal conductivity:

$\lambda = 0.6 \times (1 + w/120)(W/mK)$

Heat capacity for dry material:

$c_0 = 850 \, (J/kgK)$

Density of dry material:

$\rho_0 = 1712 \, (kg/m^3)$

Initial Conditions of Fabric: $T_0 = 15.1°C$, $w_0 = 10.58kg/m^3$.

The boundary conditions on all sides of the wall were set equal to the external conditions as measured by the Blickling weather station starting from 0000hrs on 1 July 2004.

Results

Both WuFi and Canute were used to calculate the moisture content, and RH, throughout the 600mm thickness of the test wall, (at a height of 1.5m). The comparisons at 100hrs are shown below:

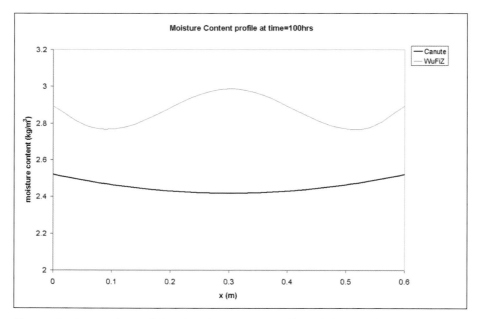

Figure 13 Comparison of simulated moisture profiles of the wall (Region 2, y=1.5) at t=100hrs for Canute ('our model') and WuFi.

The maximum difference in relative humidity between Canute and WuFi was found to be only 3.5% RH. In this simple test case there is therefore good agreement between Wufi and Canute.

In a further comparison the Canute model of the Blickling case study room was used to calculate the internal room boundary conditions, and the moisture profiles within the test wall. The test wall was the modelled in Wufi, with the same external

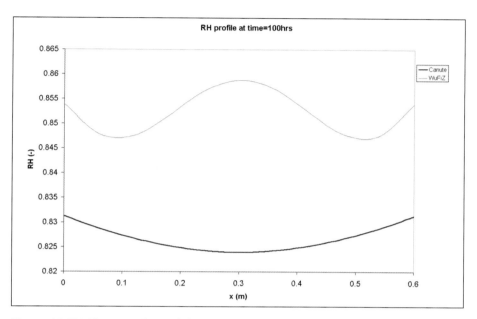

Figure 14 WuFi comparison of the relative humidity of the left wall (Region 2, y=1.5) at t=100hrs.

boundary conditions used in the Canute model, and the internal room conditions predicted by Canute for internal boundary conditions. The moisture content within the test wall, as predicted by the two models was then compared.

It can be seen that the moisture profiles produced by the two models diverge as the external surface is approached. It is probable that the WuFi prediction of falling moisture content near the external surface is the more credible in this case. Further work is required to understand the reasons for this discrepancy.

To summarise the results of the inter-model comparisons:

- The idealised test case simulated with EnergyPlus and Canute showed that Canute is able to simulate well the indoor room environment.
- In the comparison with WuFi, Canute predicts wall moisture contents of a similar order of magnitude for the Blickling and Brodick wall cross-sections, when used in decoupled mode (i.e. the indoor climate boundary conditions are input to both models rather than calculated by Canute). In fully coupled mode the Canute results are less satisfactory.

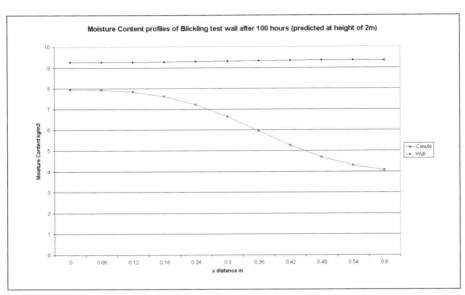

Figure 15 WuFi comparison of the moisture content of the right wall (Region 2, y=2) at t=100hrs. x distance=0 is the internal wall, x=0.6m is the external wall. It is assumed the external wall is open to the air.

■ It should be noted that such inter model comparisons cannot be seen as validation of the Canute model. There is a need for validation work using real measured data to take place.

A limitation of Canute is that it does not have the facility of WuFi to deal with driving rain as a wetting agent for the simulated wall. As a results Canute tends to overestimate the dryness of the building fabric, compared with WuFi.

In order to overcome these limitations further work beyond the timescale of Engineering Historic Futures is required. It was therefore decided to amend the project methodology and to use existing modelling tools such as EnergyPlus and WuFi to simulate the drying and climate change scenarios that the project is studying. In this methodology instead of using a single coupled model, the building simulation package EnergyPlus is used to generate the indoor boundary conditions, which are then used as an input for WuFi to simulate the wall properties.

The results presented in the second part of this report have been generated by this method.

4. Results of WUFI modelling of wall moisture content

The established WuFi HAM model was used to simulate the moisture content of the wall fabric of the sandstone walls of Brodick Castle, using as inputs the externally measured and internally measured climate.

From Figure 16 it can be seen that there are some similarities between measured and modelled data. Both show for instance that the lower part of the wall is saturated throughout its entire cross-section. The measurements made by the dowels can not be used for direct comparison with the modelled results. It should be stressed that this comparison is not meant to be viewed in any way as a validation, but merely a comparison with available data.

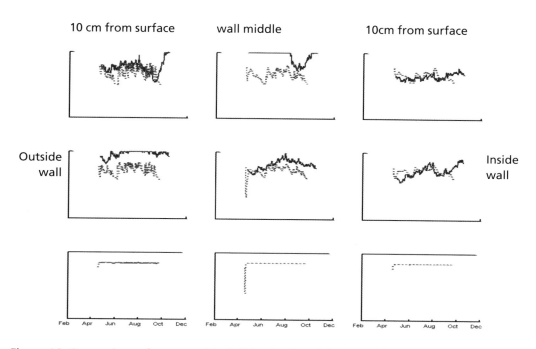

Figure 16 Comparison of measured (solid blue line) and simulated (dotted red line) moisture contents for Brodick Castle west wall, 2005. The graphs represent a cross section through the wall with the 3 x 3 (height x depth) matrix of measurement points replicated by the wall moisture model in WuFi. The measured data is plotted as hourly dowel moisture content, on an arbitrary scale. The simulated data is as hourly % moisture content on a scale of 0–6% MC by weight.

5. Simulation of effects of climate change on Blickling and Brodick building fabric

In order to predict the moisture content and temperature profiles within the external walls in the tower of Brodick Castle and the basement room of Blickling Hall, simulations were carried out using WuFi-2D. Walls thought to be representative of the external wall in the Brodick Castle and Blickling Hall basement rooms were modelled in WuFi. The assembly of the walls are shown in Figures 17 and 18, below. It should be noted that the real walls will be quite inhomogeneous, with the exact dimensions and thicknesses of different materials and layers being unknown. It was not possible to simulate the effect of banked earth against the Blickling walls so the model treats the external wall surfaces as though they are open to the air. Therefore the modelled cross-sections are to be treated as generic simulations of the types of wall at Blickling Hall and Brodick Castle rather than exact models of these walls. The results, however, should be indicative of the sort of change that may be expected at the two locations. For each wall the moisture content was output from the simulation at several points in the wall cross-section, at a height of 1.5m up the wall.

Modelled data of future climate were available from the Building Knowledge for Climate Change (BKCC) project BETWIXT, which had generated datasets of hourly climate data for south west Scotland and eastern England on behalf of EHF. The datasets used were for the 1970s (baseline period), 2020s (near future) and 2080s (far future). These data were used to generate the WuFi weather files for the future projections. The types of climate change that can be expected in these locations have been summarised by Cassar and Pender (2005) and described in more detail by Cassar (2005). The summary statistics in Tables 1 and 2 give an indication of the changes in various climate parameters used in our building simulation model predicted in the BETWIXT climate change scenarios.

External boundary conditions

The boundary conditions applied to the walls in WuFi consist of hourly values of internal (room) and external (outside weather), air temperature and relative humidity. The solar radiation and rainfall incident on the external surface are also included. The boundary conditions were created using real measured data from the test sites. The external boundary conditions were taken from the on site weather stations which measured, air temperature relative humidity, wind speed and direction, rainfall on a horizontal surface, global and diffuse solar radiation.

The weather file tool in WuFi was used to covert the readings from the site weather stations into WuFi format. The orientation and inclination of the walls, along with the geographic location of the test site were entered. The weather tool then generated the solar radiation incident on the external surface, using the global and diffuse radiation measured on a horizontal plane, and the rain incident on the wall surface, using the measured horizontal precipitation, wind speed and wind direction. The external boundary conditions for the BETWIXT scenarios were generated in a similar manner, using the BETWIXT data as input to the WuFi weather generating tool. It should be noted that the BETWIXT scenarios did not include changes to predicted wind directions.

Table 1. BETWIXT climate mean data for eastern England, used in the simulation for the Blickling Hall wall fabric

	1970s			2020s			2080s		
	T°C	RH	VP(Pa)	T°C	RH	VP(Pa)	T°C	RH	VP(Pa)
J	4.0	84%	677	5.2	82%	718	6.0	79%	735
F	4.3	82%	671	6.3	76%	714	5.9	74%	680
M	5.4	83%	732	7.4	78%	796	9.0	75%	849
A	7.9	78%	826	7.5	81%	832	12.0	65%	905
M	11.9	80%	1101	12.2	78%	1106	14.5	70%	1149
J	14.8	76%	1271	12.8	84%	1226	18.5	64%	1360
J	15.7	81%	1424	18.6	73%	1557	21.0	65%	1614
A	15.2	78%	1332	17.5	75%	1491	20.4	64%	1514
S	14.1	80%	1280	14.7	77%	1271	18.1	65%	1341
O	9.2	83%	958	11.1	80%	1049	14.7	66%	1097
N	6.6	85%	821	7.4	84%	860	13.2	64%	961
D	5.2	89%	776	6.2	82%	767	8.5	75%	829

Table 2. BETWIXT climate mean data for south west Scotland, used in the simulation for the Brodick Castle wall fabric

	1970s			2020s			2080s		
	T°C	RH	VP(Pa)	T°C	RH	VP(Pa)	T°C	RH	VP(Pa)
J	2.7	87%	641	4.0	81%	657	7.0	79%	789
F	3.8	81%	642	4.6	81%	683	6.3	76%	712
M	5.6	77%	691	5.3	80%	708	7.0	74%	732
A	7.2	76%	766	7.7	76%	795	9.6	71%	844
M	10.4	76%	945	12.5	69%	992	12.4	69%	987
J	13.0	76%	1127	13.2	73%	1100	14.9	71%	1186
J	13.2	83%	1246	16.2	75%	1380	17.8	68%	1365
A	13.4	84%	1279	15.2	73%	1259	16.8	68%	1285
S	11.0	80%	1036	12.7	80%	1168	14.0	70%	1104
O	7.9	86%	904	8.1	84%	897	10.3	77%	961
N	6.2	80%	754	6.3	80%	752	7.9	75%	785
D	5.1	87%	753	6.4	81%	770	7.5	78%	800

Internal boundary conditions

For the modelling using present day conditions, the monitored data from the test rooms were used as the internal boundary conditions. For the BETWIXT scenarios internal boundary conditions were generated using the building simulation software EnergyPlus. The BETWIXT data were transformed into EnergyPlus weather files which were then used in simulation to predict internal temperatures in the rooms. Unlike CANUTE Energy Plus cannot model the flow of moisture between the fabric and the room. In order to model the effect of the moisture-laden walls on the room relative humidity, a source of moisture was included in the room model, the magnitude of which was comparing model results for 2005 with measure room conditions.

The results of the simulation of future climate change on the walls are shown in Figures 19–21, which compare the wall moisture contents for the 1970s base period, 2020s and 2080s. At Blickling (Figure 19) in the 1970s and 2020s the external climate has remarkably little effect on the wall moisture content, which remains at approximately 12% throughout the year. It is only in the 2080s that any climate change effects are seen, when drying through the entire wall cross-section

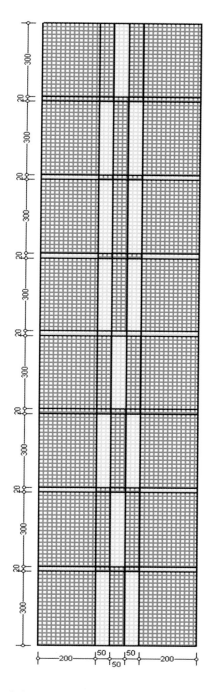

Figure 17 Schematic diagram of the sandstone wall of Brodick Castle, as simulated in WuFi with dimensions of the elements in mm. Note that mortar joints between the sandstone blocks are part of the simulation. A rubble core is included in the model, based on experimental observations of the Brodick wall.

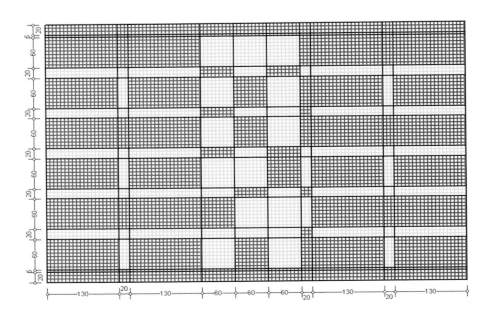

Figure 18 Schematic diagram of the brick wall of Blickling Hall, as simulated in WuFi, with dimensions of the wall elements in mm. Note that mortar joints between the bricks and the brick/mortar infill in the wall core, the presence of which was suggested from the wall core taken at Blickling.

starts to begin in the late summer, driven by the dryer hotter climate expected by this decade. Wetting and drying cycles in the wall are most pronounced at or close to the internal surface.

The effect of such a change could be to reduce the potential for mould and algal growth on the internal walls in the latter part of the year. The cycling conditions could also promote potentially damaging salt movement within the brickwork leading to salt efflorescence and surface damage or disfigurement.

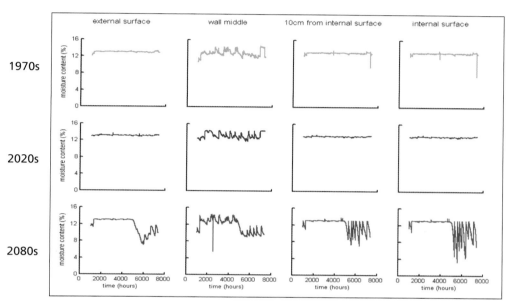

Figure 19 WuFi annual simulations of the effect of climate change on the Blickling Hall wall moisture profile, using BETWIXT data. The 1970s baseline period is shown in green, top; near future (2020s) are in blue, middle; and far future (2080s) are in red, lower. The major changes are anticipated for the 2080s when there is a considerable increase in drying at or close to the wall surfaces in the second half of the year.

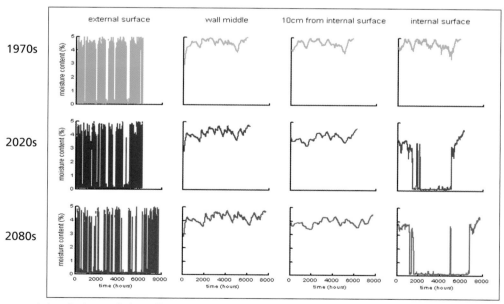

Figure 20 WuFi annual simulations of the effect of climate change on the Brodick Castle west wall moisture profile, using BETWIXT data. The 1970s baseline period is shown in green, top; near future (2020s) are in blue, middle; and far future (2080s) are in red, lower. The external wall moisture content varies enormously because of cycles of wetting from wind-driven rain and drying in the sun. The simulation suggests that there will be considerable drying at the internal surface of this west wall in the future.

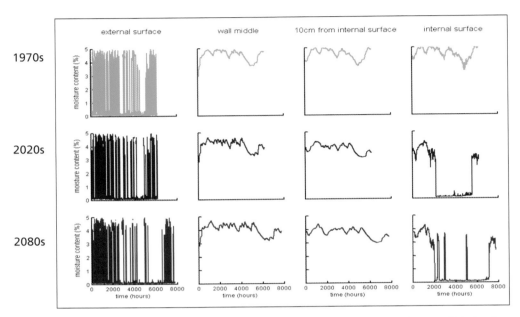

Figure 21 WuFi annual simulations of the effect of climate change on the Brodick Castle east wall moisture profile, using BETWIXT data. The 1970s baseline period is shown in green, top; near future (2020s) are in blue, middle; and far future (2080s) are in red, lower. The external wall moisture content varies enormously because of cycles of wetting from wind-driven rain and drying in the sun. The simulation suggests that there will be considerable drying at the internal surface of this west wall in the future. The wall moisture properties appear similar to those of the west wall, even though it receives a higher driving rain input than the east wall.

At Brodick the climate is characterised in all the modelled decades by many cycles of wetting and drying of the external surface due to driving rain. The internal wall moisture content varies little despite changes in the internal and external climate. At the internal wall surface some change is apparent in the 2020s and 2080s as a result of summer drying, when the surface moisture content falls to almost zero. Driving rain on the external wall surface in the 2020s rarely penetrates to wet the internal surface, in contrast to Blickling, where internal surface wetting and drying cycles are far more frequent. This reflects the sandstone wall's greater resistance to water penetration compared to the more porous brickwork at Blickling.

The modelling suggests that in the future the Brodick type of wall construction may experience drier internal surfaces during summer, which could be beneficial for restricting mould and algal growth, and that driving rain effects on walls in this part of Scotland will be similar to what is currently experienced.

6. Simulation of forced drying of building fabric

The WuFi models of the Blickling Hall and Brodick Castle test rooms described in section 5 were used to investigate the forced drying of the wall fabric. The strategy modelled was similar to that employed at Blickling Hall and in the laboratory test wall drying experiments using equipment supplied by Munters Dehumidification Ltd. The strategy was to heat the air mass adjacent to the wet wall to 40°C, which was assumed to result in a relative humidity of 20% in the air at the wall.

The external climate measurements from Blickling and Brodick for 2005 were used to set the external boundary conditions. The indoor boundary conditions were the drying conditions of 40°C and 20% RH. It was assumed that drying began in January and continued until November. The initial moisture content of the Blickling wall was set at 12% and that for the Brodick wall at 5%.

Figures 22 and 23 show the effect of forced drying on the wall surface and at points in the wall cross-section for Blickling and Brodick, respectively.

For both walls the drying strategy quickly reduces surface moisture content. At Blickling after 6 weeks the moisture content 10cm from the internal surface is predicted to have reduced from 10% by mass to 4% by mass and the moisture content of the centre of the wall is reduced to approximately 10% by mass. When rain penetrates the external surface it can be seen to increase the moisture content of the wall and even to raise the moisture content of the internal surface. Moisture from the ground would therefore also be expected to increase the moisture content of these cross-sections.

At Brodick the drying has less effect on the bulk of the wall – at 10cm into the wall the moisture content is still around 3% after several months of drying, when the internal surface is completely dry. Even though driving rain on the external wall at Brodick is far higher than at Blickling, it has a much lesser effect on the wall bulk or internal surface properties. This occurs because the Blickling brick wall is more porous and water can move through it more rapidly than through the sandstone wall.

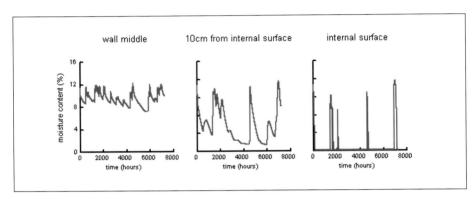

Figure 22 Simulated drying of the Blickling Hall wall fabric.

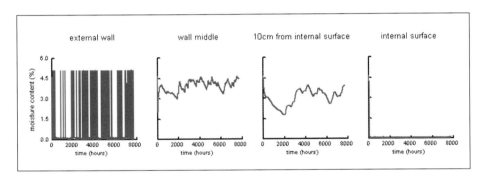

Figure 23 Simulated drying of the Brodick Castle wall fabric

7. Summary of scientific findings of the modelling work

A methodology has been developed for using climate change data with building simulation models to try and understand how climate change may affect buildings in the future. However the following limitations must be recognised in the modelling that has been undertaken:

- The room and fabric models are not fully coupled
- Driving rain algorithm in WuFi is simplistic
- The BETWIXT scenarios produce 30 years of data, but only 1 year of which could be used in WuFi. It is not certain that the year used is representative of the whole period
- The BETWIXT data set does not include wind direction data
- The WuFi models are 2D slices of walls, complicated geometries cannot be

considered, nor can the effect of banked earth against the wall be easily modelled

The Canute model has a number of limitations that have prevented its use, as yet, in the modelling applications of the project. Further work will take place to improve the model so that a coupled model is completed. These aspects will be reported in the final project report.

Moisture modelling of the fabric and climate of buildings is one of the most complex and least understood areas of building science. The complexity, particularly for historic buildings, results from the following:

i. Accurate moisture modelling requires accurate modelling of temperature as well as moisture, making the modelling an order of magnitude more difficult than modelling of temperature alone.
ii. The mechanics of moisture transport are varied and complicated, involving capillary movement as liquid and movement in the vapour phase, driving rain, flooding and ground contact.
iii. The physical characteristics of materials that affect moisture movement and storage are both complex and poorly defined for most materials, particularly historic materials.
iv. The liquid transport coefficients are measured during wetting experiments. The values used for these coefficients during drying are estimates.
v. Building fabric moisture measurements to test the validity of models are difficult to collect and as this project has shown collecting time-resolved data to validate building simulation programmes is particularly problematic. The dowel building fabric moisture measurement method used in EHF is often applied to historic buildings and can give adequate results over a long averaging period, but the electrical resistance measurement method for short-term data was not successful. New methods are being developed to overcome these problems
vi. Ventilation plays a critical role in moisture transport and this parameter is also notoriously difficult to measure.

During the EHF project a world-wide comparative exercise to test building models against each other and against measured data has begun (IEA Annex 41). EHF has participated in this comparison and made useful inputs to the Annex, which will continue until 2007. Within the context of the international comparison the Canute model has the potential to be a world-leading model.

Models such as Canute are inevitably simplifications, and many assumptions and compromises have to be included in their development. Results of such models should always be treated with caution. In the development of such models it is important to state the limitations that exist and to conduct clear and transparent testing and, when possible, validation. Users can then make informed decisions as to whether they wish to use such models, and the level of confidence that can be placed on model predictions. That being said, models such as Wufi have been widely used to investigate drying in masonry walls (Kunzel *et al* 1996, 1998), and provide an interesting method of investigating such problems.

Bearing in mind these limitations the following conclusions can be drawn from this research:

Broadly, the modelling indicates that there will be little change in the conditions of either the sandstone or brick walls in the future. There is some evidence of drying on the internal surfaces of the walls, but the effect should be treated with caution, bearing in mind the uncertainties of the modelling process. Such a change could lead to more rapid movement of salts in porous brickwork of the type modelled and surface salt efflorescences as the moisture content of the masonry changes. In the Scottish sandstone wall modelled there are far fewer cycles of changing moisture content except at the internal and external surfaces, so salt movement may be less.

The BETWIXT data did not show any increase in the effect of driving rain in south west Scotland, and the overall effect suggested by the modelling completed so far is that there is a greater tendency for drying of the stone building fabric than wetting.

The modelling suggests that water transport is far more rapid in the brick wall that the sandstone wall. This type of historic brick fabric is therefore more vulnerable to water penetration to its internal surface than the stone wall fabric, even though in the modelling the stone wall is subject to a far higher incidence of driving rain.

Further work is required to compare the results of simulation with those of experimental measurements in order to understand the effects of different drying strategies and what may be optimal approach for historic building fabric.

9. References

BETWIXT (2006) http://www.cru.uea.ac.uk/projects/betwixt/ Accessed 9/08/06.

Cassar, M. (2005) *Climate Change and the Historic Environment*, London, English Heritage.

Cassar, M. and Pender, R. (2005) The impact of climate change on cultural heritage: evidence and response. In Preprints of the ICOM Committee for Conservation 14th Triennial Meeting, The Hague, 12–16 September 2005, Vol. 2. Edited by Verger, I. pp. 610–616. James & James, London.

ECBCS (2006) http://www.ecbcs.org/annexes/annex41.htm Accessed 9/08/06.

EnergyPlus (2006) http://www.eere.energy.gov/buildings/energyplus/ Accessed 9/08/06.

Wufi (2006) http://www.hoki.ibp.fraunhofer.de Accessed 31/07/06.

EnergyPlus (Testing and validation) (2006)
http://www.eere.energy.gov/buildings/energyplus/testing.html Accessed 20/11/06

Wufi (testing and validation) (2006) http://www.hoki.ibp.fhg.de/wufi/validierung_e.html Accessed 20/11/06.

Hagentoft C, 1999. Hamstad, Detemination of liquid water transfer properties of porous building materials and development of numerical assessment methods. Chalmers University of Technology, Sweden. Report R-02:9.

Annex 41, 2006, http://www.kuleuven.ac.be/bwf/projects/annex41/index.htm Accessed 20/11/06

Künzel, H.M., Kießl, K. Drying of brick walls after impregnation. Internationale Zeitschrift für Bauinstandsetzen 2 (1996) H. 2, S. 87–100.

Künzel, H.M. Drying of Masonry with Exterior Insulation. Proceedings of the Fifth International Masonry Conference. British Masonry Society, No. 8, Stoke-on-Trent 1998, pp 245–250

6 Quantifying the costs of climate change impacts on the built heritage

Tim Taylor,[1] Alistair Hunt,[1] May Cassar[2] and Ian Wainwright[3]

[1] Department of Economics and International Development University of Bath, Bath BA2 7AY
[2] UCL Centre for Sustainable Heritage, The Bartlett School of Graduate Studies (Torrington Place Site), University College London, Gower Street, London WC1E 6BT
[3] Ecclesiastical Insurance Group plc, Beaufort House, Brunswick Road, Gloucester GL1 1JZ

Introduction

Climate change is likely to have a significant impact on the cultural heritage sector. With increased flood risk, increased frequency of storms and risks of summer drought, the stock of buildings of historic and cultural significance is likely to be hit hard by climate related impacts.

As part of the research project Engineering Historic Futures, funded by the Engineering and Physical Science Research Council and the United Kingdom Climate Impacts Programme, we attempted to quantify the direct and indirect costs of climate impacts on the built heritage. Quantitative information on the sectoral costs of climate change are likely to be useful in determining where adaptation initiatives should be focused since policy on climate change adaptation invariably involves trade-offs in the use of scarce resources.

The climate variable we have focused on is precipitation and we considered the flooding of historic buildings as the socio-economic impact. We were concerned with the cost of post-flood adaptation not pre-flood adaptation, and we specifically evaluated two historic buildings at a local level and not flood damage in general. Initially we set out to establish the cost differential between different rates of drying and how successful different drying regimes are both directly and indirectly. For reasons which will become clear in the next section, we widened our approach beyond direct physical damage to property such as loss of value and revenue which include the repair costs of damage, temporary relocation costs such as hire of alternative accommodation, additional travel expenses and additional staffing, services, facilities, etc., and loss of revenue and additional administration costs. We evaluated the cost of losses to the intrinsic value and future attraction of cultural heritage that together with the cost to human health are indirect factors affecting total costs in relation to the number of heritage buildings and their distribution in relation to flood risk.

Cost of different rates of drying

There are essentially three ways to dry buildings:

- Dehumidification (desiccant (sometimes called adsorption) or refrigerant)
- Air movement (using fans)
- Gross ventilation by letting natural air movement do the work (only feasible in spring and summer in the UK)

The combination of dehumidification and air movement can also be used.

In costing different rates of drying, the variables that arise make it difficult to draw general conclusions. Business Continuity Network Limited has summarised the factors that come into play in a series of questions: *'Are the premises habitable, or preferably habitable? ...What has got wet, how wet, how long, how much, type of water, grey or rain, construction materials, how fast etc. etc.? Why are we drying? Prevent mould or corrosion as well? ...Every situation is different.'*[1]

The answers to these questions will determine the drying regime that is selected in different situations.

The cost of drying also depends on what is meant by dry. The socio-economic definition of *dry* is 'dry enough for the purpose'. The purpose can be defined as 'what is going to happen to the material now' which will vary from one situation to another. So the drying method chosen will depend on many factors including the performance of equipment under different conditions. For example, refrigerant dehumidification is inefficient in cold environments where desiccant dehumidifiers alone or combined with air movement might be preferred. It is evident that the rate of drying will depend on all of these factors as well as the materials, type of building and its condition.

We concluded that the only realistic method of costing different rates of drying would be to compare of how different companies estimate their costs which include by the cubic capacity of a room, by the square meters of a surface, by the artifact or building element or by a charge on a time and materials basis with an additional rental charge for the drying equipment. Furthermore, we concluded that the cost of different rates of drying can only be estimated for specific situations by asking what the advantages are of drying in a particular way. In the case of historic buildings, financial savings and saving in time will need to be balanced against the loss of intrinsic value and future attraction of different rates of drying. Faster drying may imply reduced costs in terms of disruption, but may imply significant long term costs in terms of future repairs or the loss of features of interest – and any complete economic appraisal would need to take these factors into account.

As a consequence of the above, a simple generic cost-effectiveness analysis would not be appropriate to identify the general ranking of different technologies, given the fact that differing conditions and uses of buildings may affect the impacts of flood damage and the effects that drying technologies may have on the uses of buildings and on the building fabric itself. This is an area that needs more research. In the light of these issues, we develop a case study of two historic buildings that have been previously affected by flooding and which had to be dried. This is used as a means of valuing future flood risks to the two buildings under different climate change scenarios. This gives an indication of current and future costs once the drying technology has been chosen for the given site.

Costing method for historic buildings: a case study[2]

This case study provides estimates of future climate-induced costs of flooding of two churches in Lewes using an historical analogue of the October 2000 floods. We estimated the following:

■ *The total undiscounted costs of climate change induced flood damage to the two churches* over the period 2011 to 2100 – with no adaptive measures beyond simple repair of the damage – *range from £310,000 to £750,000* (constant 2003 prices). This represents between a 50% and 340% increase over the time period.

- *The total present value (i.e. discounted) cost of climate change induced flooding over the period 2011–2100 range from £35,000 to £90,000* (constant 2003 pounds).*

- These cost estimates are likely to under-estimate the full welfare costs of flood-related climate costs to these buildings because they do not directly account for the welfare losses associated with e.g. disruption to church services and resulting change in travel time and other costs, and the loss of heritage value.

- It is not appropriate to consider adaptation measures for the two heritage buildings independently of all the other properties likely to be included in a local appraisal of flood risk policies that incorporate climate scenarios. Nevertheless, it is important that account is taken of the non-costed welfare effects in any adaptation appraisal process.

Context

In this case study we made some initial estimates of the economic welfare costs associated with the impacts on heritage buildings that might result under future climate change scenarios. Impacts on heritage buildings are likely to arise from a range of changes in climate variables including increased precipitation in winters and associated floods, possible increased incidence of storms and increased humidity.

This issue first attracted attention with an English Heritage funded scoping study undertaken by the UCL Centre for Sustainable Heritage.[3] The focus of this case study is on the impact costs of increased precipitation in winters and associated floods under climate change scenarios on two historically significant buildings. In order to make these cost estimates we take the floods of October 2000 as an historical analogue.

* These totals are calculated for the two scenarios by multiplying the average annual cost identified for the three time periods by the 30 years within each period.

Flooding in Lewes, West Sussex had an impact on two buildings of cultural importance. Jireh Chapel is a wood-built church and St Thomas à Becket church is a stone building in the Cliffe area of Lewes. Both churches are used by local residents as places of worship and have attributes that are unique, some of which were damaged in the flooding. The characteristics of these churches are described in Box 1. In addition to damages to these churches, 129 Grade II listed buildings and 230 buildings in the town's conservation area were damaged.

The case study structure describes firstly the method by which climate change impacts on cultural heritage can be estimated; secondly, these impacts are considered in relation to a decision-making framework and finally, the treatment of uncertainty is considered.

> **Box 1:**
>
> **Characteristics of Churches affected in Lewes**
>
> **St Thomas à Becket** at Cliffe is a small Anglican parish church. It is steeped in history, dating back to the 12th century. The body and tower of the church date from the 14th and 15th centuries, while a vestry was added in the 19th century.
>
> **Jireh Chapel** was built in 1805 in an American Colonial style, mainly of timber with a timber frame. The foundations rest on a bed of chalk and its roof is held together by wooden pegs. It is clad with Welsh slate on the South side, Weather tiles on the West side and the unique Sussex Mathematical tiles on the North and Eastern faces. The Chapel was the base for the preacher William Huntingdon (1745–1813). The Chapel is typical of a Georgian Non-Conformist place of worship, with the pulpit being the central feature. Most of the original fitted box and family pews are still in place, along with the Grand Pew which is immediately below the pulpit, on which elders and deacons would sit. The Chapel is occasionally visited by tour groups and is the place of worship of a small group of Protestant Dissenters of the Calvinistic Persuasion, led by the Pastor Noel Shields of the Free Presbyterian Church. It is a Grade 1 listed building.

Application of the costing guidelines
Impact Assessment

In this section we show how the costs associated with preserving the built heritage under a climate change scenario may be estimated. We employ the UKCIP Costing Method . Figure 1 gives a graphical illustration of the approach taken in this study. We first identify the impacts if there is no climate change (the reference scenario). The projected reference scenario shows that costs to heritage sites may increase irrespective of climate change.

We first selected a relevant impact from one of the matrices in the UKCIP Costing Method Implementation Report . The impact matrices are used to provide a first indication of the types of impacts that need to be considered, a link to the most

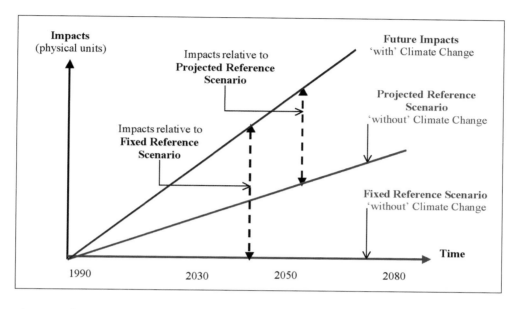

Figure 1 Illustration of Reference Scenarios: Valuing the Impact of Climate Change
Source: Adapted from Parry and Carter (1998)

appropriate valuation guideline to employ, and the stakeholder groups who are most likely to be involved in any decision-making process that incorporates the costing analysis. In this case study, the *Buildings and Infrastructure Sector Matrix* can be used, where the initial climate change impact is the *Increased Frequency of Storms and Flooding*. The relevant section of the matrix is replicated below in Table 1, for illustration, with the particular row highlighted in bold.

Table 1 Extract from Climate Change Impact Matrix: Increased Frequency of Storms and Flooding

Direct Impact	VM	Potential Indirect Impact	VM	Sector Affected	VM	Potential Sectoral Impact	VM	Relevant Stakeholders
Direct physical impact (NT)		Damage	CO	Transport infrastructure	CO	Loss of infrastructure/equipment	CO	Transport operators, contractors, local public (users and employees in this sector)
						Damage to infrastructure/equipment	CO	
				Buildings & infrastructure		Loss of property and infrastructure	CO	Households, property owners, insurers, contractors
						Damage to property and infrastructure	CO	
				Historical and cultural heritage		Loss of cultural objects	ET	**Local public, tourists, national interest groups, government and tax payers (general public), insurers**
						Damage to cultural objects	ET	
				Human health		Increased risk of accidents	IG	Local public, employers, insurers, NHS, government, regulators
						Increased risk of mortality	IG	
						Increased risk of morbidity	IG	
				Sea defence		Decreased strength, increased maintenance requirements	CO	Local authorities, government, EA, MAFF, contractors
						Damage to infrastructure	CO	
				Energy sector (coastal facilities & power distribution)		Damage to wind power and wave power	CO	Power generators, and electricity consumers (prices), regulator, insurers
						Damage to thermal and nuclear stations	CO	
						Damage to offshore oil and gas facilities	CO	Oil & gas industry, insurers, consumers (including impact on exports) and local public (environmental impacts)
						Damage to refineries	CO	
						Damage to pipelines	CO	
						Damage to electricity transmission and distribution lines	CO	Power generators, and electricity consumers (disruption), regulator, insurers

The matrix in Table 1 identifies that for the direct and indirect impacts with which we are concerned – increased precipitation and resultant flooding – valuation techniques are not available. However, the sectoral impact is in heritage property where the notation "ET" indicates that either conventional market based valuation techniques or an individual guideline may be relevant to the costing of this impact. Indeed, ideally both would be used in this case. We employ conventional market based valuation techniques in this study as little data on the non-market side was available at the time of the study.

It is important to note, however, that the choice of technique has important implications for how the resulting cost estimates can be interpreted. The use of the restoration cost technique will result in estimates of the expected costs incurred by the owners of the church and chapel in restoring the buildings to their original state after climate change induced flood damage. In contrast, there are techniques identified in Metroeconomica (2004) in which the welfare cost of the flood damage can be estimated. The welfare cost is likely to differ from the restoration cost since it aims to estimate in monetary terms how much people are willing to pay to avoid the flood damage occurring (or, conversely their willingness to accept the flood damage). For example, people may value the buildings as part of the national heritage whether or not they actually visit them. We can therefore assume that as long as the financial resources are committed to restoration, people are willing to pay at least as much as the restoration costs. In this case the restoration costs represent a minimum (lower bound) estimate of peoples' true valuation of the asset. The non-market valuation techniques described in the Individual Guideline on Cultural Objects in Metroeconomica (2004) provide ways in which the true value of the asset can be derived. However, application of these techniques is demanding in terms of the data and resource requirements which is beyond the scope for the current project.

Impact assessment

Step 1
Impact assessment using historical analogue

The first step is to measure in physical terms the damage to heritage buildings of increased flooding from climate change. In order to estimate these impacts for future years we use historical data as a benchmark. The physical impact of the flood in October 2000 in Lewes is used as an example of a flooding event, the frequency of which may change under climate scenarios. As noted above, two historic churches were flooded. The main damages are described in Box 2 opposite. Note that the physical damage is described in qualitative terms since in this context the damage does not easily fit into a quantitative unit measure. As will be described below we therefore use the restoration cost for the buildings in total rather than per square meter.

Impact assessment under future scenarios

In order to estimate the total physical impact in future time periods under climate change scenarios we need to consider how the impacts described above for October 2000 are likely to change under future socio-economic and climate scenarios. UKCIP (2001) provides the basis for socio-economic scenarios (SES) developed for climate impact assessment.

There are four distinct future scenarios, World Markets (WM), National Enterprise (NE), Local Stewardship (LS) and Global Sustainability (GS). Since we want to examine impacts to the end of the century, two methods may be used to generate impact estimates for the time-slice centred on the 2080s: one based on linear extrapolation, the other simply using the data for the 2050s.** For simplicity, in this case study we report only the results from the linear extrapolation of existing trends in the variables, from 2020s through the 2050s[†] to the 2080s.

**Note that the linear intensification of the trends identified between the 2020s and the 2050s has the advantage of working with trends that have already been verified in producing the UKCIP SES whilst the use of 2050s values for the 2080s does not require any extrapolation that has not been critically reviewed and verified.
[†]Quantitative estimates of household size are only provided for the 2020s. We therefore also make projections for this variable for the 2050s and 2080s on the basis of linear intensification of existing trends or use of values found for the 2020s.

Box 2

Impacts of October 2000 floods on Heritage Buildings in Lewes

St Thomas à Becket

Flood damage to pews and other furnishings of church. Floor of church had to be cleaned and repaired after sludge damage.

Jireh Chapel

Major flood damage to floor of chapel, with timber raised by one foot in places. Damage to pews and to flooring, with contaminated sludge covering the area. Loss of books, sound equipment and damage to pulpit and walls. The church building was closed for three weeks, with repairs ongoing for a ten week period. Major costs are described in the Annex at the end of the report. Below are photographs of the damage to the church. The contaminated sludge on floors can be seen in the first photograph, whilst the damage to the pew areas and flooring can be seen. Staining to the wood of the pews can be seen on the right-hand side of the second photograph.

Figure 2 Interior view of St Thomas à Becket

Figure 3 Flood damage to Jireh Chapel
© Noel Shields

Figure 4 Flood damage to Jireh Chapel – some staining can be seen
© Noel Shields

Interpretation of socio-economic scenarios

The principal socio-economic factors that may be expected to determine exposure of heritage properties to flood risk include:

- heritage insurance policy related to properties at flood risk
- degree of preventive flood protection measures, and
- numbers of properties defined as *heritage*.

The qualitative information in the scenarios that relates to the factors listed is difficult to interpret in quantitative terms. We have therefore given a qualitative indication in Table 2 as to whether we think the individual factors are likely to increase or decrease the total damage to heritage properties flooded. Note that "+ve" implies a trend towards greater vulnerability whilst a "-ve" implies less vulnerability. So, for example, there is assumed to be less concern for heritage preservation under World Markets and National Enterprise scenarios, thereby making it less likely that resources will be spent on their maintenance and increasing their vulnerability. Thus, our interpretation of the World Markets and National Enterprise scenarios leads us to conclude that heritage properties will on balance be more vulnerable to flood risk whilst the opposite would be true under the Local Stewardship and Global Sustainability scenarios. The corollary of this is that because social preferences under World Market and National Enterprise scenarios show a move away from heritage preservation there are likely to be less properties maintained. Thus, one might expect less total damage to heritage properties but more damage to those properties still preserved.

The main impact on costs of repair to churches as a result of changes in socioeconomic conditions is likely to be from changes in GDP growth. Here we have assumed that energy prices and architects fees will rise in line with GDP per capita. GDP per capita rises most quickly under the World Markets scenario, with incomes rising by almost 400% by the 2050s (see Table 3). These growth rates can be applied to the unit costs used in the derivation of total restoration costs.

Table 2 Qualitative indicators of effect of socio-economic factors on flood damage to heritage properties under alternative SESs

Socio-economic factor	Socio-economic scenario			
	LS	NE	WM	GS
Social preferences for heritage preservation	– ve	+ ve	+ ve	– ve
Flood protection policy	– ve	+ ve	– ve	– ve
Insurance policy	?	?	+ ve	– ve
Overall net effect	– ve	+ ve	+ ve	– ve
+ ve implies greater vulnerability; – ve implies less vulnerability				

Table 3 GDP per capita under UKCIP SES

	1990s	2003	2020s		2050s	
			LS	WM	LS	WM
GDP/ca	10500	12302	15000	24000	24000	61000
% change from 1990s			21.9	95.1	95.1	395.8

Changes in probabilities of dry and warm summer weather events under climate change scenarios

As part of the physical impact assessment we need to assess how the frequency (or probability) of a given climate event changes under alternative climate scenarios. This will allow us to calculate expected values in the subsequent monetary valuation of these impacts.

By the 2080s, under the UKCIP02 Medium-High Emissions Scenario , 7% of years will experience a wet "1994–5 type" winter. The UKCIP02 report does not contain information on Autumn 2000 but similar precipitation patterns were recorded in the winter of 1994–5 and so we assume for our purposes that they are approximately equivalent. The report contains multiplying factors for the conversion from 2080s Medium-High Emissions scenario* to other scenarios and

* UKCIP (April 2002) Climate Change Scenarios for the United Kingdom. page 39.

Table 4 Percentage of years experiencing wet 1994/5 winter type* conditions in high and low climate scenarios													
	Baseline (no CC)	2020s				2050s				2080s			
Emissions Scenario		Low	M-L	M-H	High	Low	M-L	M-H	High	Low	M-L	M-H	High
% of years	1.00	1.00	1.00	1.00	1.07	2.26	2.63	3.00	3.58	4.27	4.97	7.00	8.26
Probabilities	0.01	0.01	0.01	0.01	0.01	0.02	0.03	0.03	0.04	0.04	0.05	0.07	0.08

M-L = Medium-Low; M-H = Medium-High

time-slices. Using these multiplying factors the probability of a wet *1994–5 type* winter have been calculated for three 30-year time slices, centred on the 2020s, 2050s and 2080s, under the four climate scenarios. The results are shown in Table 3. The probabilities given are used to calculate expected values, as described below.

Economic valuation

Step 2: Restoration costs
The second step is to identify and estimate the expenditure incurred to replace (or restore) the asset damaged as a result of climate change, in unit cost terms.

Estimation of repair costs
Repair costs for St Thomas à Becket were estimated at £100,000. These costs included cleaning of the church and pews and replacement of items lost due to the flooding.

For Jireh Chapel, costs of repair were estimated at £128,000. Damages included repair to woodwork, electrical equipment and the contents of the church.

* 66% wetter than average

In these two cases, therefore, the unit is the building as a whole.

Step 3: Ancillary benefits and costs

The third step is to indicate the value of ancillary benefits/costs that can be subtracted from the value derived in step two. In this case it is assumed that the expenditure spent on building repair is a perfect substitute for the climate change impact incurred i.e. flooding of buildings resulting from a wet autumn/winter.

As was noted above when discussing the choice of using the replacement/restoration guideline or the individual guideline on cultural objects, there are a number of non-financial welfare costs that are not included in this cost estimate. These include:

- costs of relocation of church services during repair work, including costs of travel or hire of facilities
- loss of heritage value due to damage (or repair) of heritage buildings
- loss of time to church wardens and ministers in administering repair work.

Estimation of the loss of heritage value would require the use of non-market valuation techniques which is beyond the scope of this study. The alternative is to transfer results from an existing study (or studies) to the present context, assuming that the subject of the original study is similar to the present context. A preliminary search of the literature revealed that no previous studies on flooding in churches could be found. Studies do exist on the cleaning of churches as a consequence of air pollution, but it was not felt that these estimates would be transferable to the context of flooding, due to the specific nature of the buildings considered and the type of damage.

In addition, any longer term impacts on the church buildings of being exposed to flood waters are not considered. Even with restoration, there are potential long term effects of the exposure of materials to flood waters – for example the cupping of floor boards which may affect the life of flooring,

Step 4: Estimation of total cost of climate change impacts

Step 4 is to calculate the total cost of the climate change impact for the different climate scenarios. The predicted increase in the frequency of wet winters like 1994/5 was provided in Table 4 and the Low and High Emission Scenario values for the 2020s, 2050s and the 2080s are used. The baseline period (i.e. the period without climate change) is taken as the conventional 30-year period 1961–1990. Without climate change it has been assumed that a wet winter such as 1994–5 was a 1 in 100 year event i.e. had a 1% probability of occurring.

It is assumed that the costs of the resulting structural maintenance repair and for replacing items damaged are largely unaffected by changes in socio-economic scenarios over time. However, costs for architects fees and electricity were assumed to vary with GDP.

For the baseline (no climate change) case, total annual flooding costs in Table 5 are calculated by multiplying the repair cost for both buildings under the socio-economic scenarios identified above by the probability of such a wet weather event occurring without climate change – the 1 in 100 case. Note that we assume no further GDP/capita growth beyond the 2050s.

Unit damage cost X probability of weather event (no climate change)

For the future climate change scenarios, the totals in Table 6 are derived by multiplying costs of repair by the probability of such a wet weather event occurring under low and high climate change emission scenarios for the different time periods, as given in Table 4. In this calculation, the costs derived from the Local Stewardship and Global Markets socio-economic scenarios are matched with the low and high climate change emission scenarios, respectively.

Table 5 Total annual flooding costs to Jireh Chapel and St Thomas à Becket Church, Lewes under alternative socio-economic scenarios – no climate change (£, 2004 prices)

2020s		2050s		2080s		
LS	WM	LS	WM	LS	WM	
2293	2300	2300	2500	2300	2500	

Unit damage cost X probability of weather event (with climate change)

Table 6 Total annual flooding costs to Jireh Chapel and St Thomas à Becket church, Lewes under alternative socio-economic scenarios – with climate change (£, 2004 prices)						
2020s		2050s		2080s		
LS	WM	LS	WM	LS	WM	
2293	2509	5287	8997	9976	20764	

Table 7 shows the net additional annual cost induced by climate change i.e. the costs presented in Table 5 subtracted from those in Table 6.

Table 6 total costs – Table 5 total costs = net costs in Table 7

Table 7 Net total climate change costs of flooding to Jireh Chapel and St Thomas à Becket church, Lewes (£, 2004 prices)						
2020s		2050s		2080s		
LS	WM	LS	WM	LS	WM	
0	209	2951	6483	7639	18250	

From Table 7, the total net undiscounted cost of flooding for the two buildings over the period 2011–2100 is calculated as being between £310,000 (Low/LS scenarios) and £750,000 (High/WM scenarios) compared to between £210,000 and £220,000 under non-climate change scenarios. This represents an increase in total costs over the time period of between 50% and 340%.

Discounting

Discounting is the conventional approach used by economists to weight and add environmental costs and benefits that occur at different points in time. Discounting arises because individuals are observed to attach less weight to a benefit or cost in the future than they do to a benefit or cost now. Referring to the Treasury's Green Book,* a discount rate of 3.5% should be applied to impacts

*http://greenbook.treasury.gov.uk/

occurring in 0–30 years from present, 3.0% for 31–75 years and 2.5% for 76–125 years. The discount rate determines the weight assigned to the climate-induced cost in each future year.*

When discounting is applied to the annual climate change induced costs the values fall significantly, as Table 7 shows. However the costs given in Table 7 are still around 17 times higher in the 2080s than the 2020s under a WM/High Emissions scenario.

Table 8 Discounted annual costs of climate change						
2020s		2050s		2080s		
LS	WM	LS	WM	LS	WM	
0	86	575	1264	632	1510	

On the basis of the annual costs given in Table 8, (and using the same method to calculate totals described under Table 5), we calculate that *the total present value (i.e. discounted) cost of climate change induced flooding over the period 2011–2100 – with no adaptive measures beyond straight repair of the damage – range from £35,000 to £90,000.***

The total present value of flooding over the period 2011–2100 without climate change is calculated by discounting the figures of £210,000 and £220,000 presented below Table 5 and is approximately £55,000. Hence, the present value of flooding damage including climate change is estimated to be between £90,000 and £145,000.

---

* The weight, or discount factor, to be assigned to costs in any given year is calculated as follows. The discount factor in year t is equal to: 1 / (1 + discount rate in year 1) * 1 / (1 + discount rate in year 2) * 1 / (1 + discount rate in year 3) * ...... * 1 / (1 + discount rate in year t minus 1) * 1 / (1 + discount rate in year t).
** These totals are calculated for the two scenarios by multiplying the average annual cost identified for the three time periods by the 30 years within each period.

Non-monetised impacts

As mentioned earlier, there are a number of non-monetised impacts associated with flooding to churches and other historic buildings. The lack of a monetary estimate for these climate change impacts does not mean that those impacts can be overlooked in any decision-making process. A simple checklist can be constructed which serves to identify all potential impacts relevant to the decision at hand, and indicate whether or not each impact can or would be monetised. For our case study, Table 9 shows such a checklist.

In the absence of monetary estimates of such damages (as can be obtained from primary contingent valuation studies or appropriate use of the benefit-transfer technique), decision making frameworks such as multi-criteria analysis which enable the consideration of non-monetary impacts side by side with monetary estimates may be used.

Table 9 'Checklist' for the identification of all impacts of relevance: example of damage to heritage buildings				
	4th Order Impact	**Valuation**		
		NO	**YES**	
Item	Cost of repair		√	
	Disruption to church services:			
	Change in travel time and other costs	√		
	Loss of heritage value from repair	√		
	Time of administration of repair	√		
	Longer term impacts of flooding	√		

Uncertainty

It is useful to highlight the sources of uncertainty that have necessarily been incorporated in this costing analysis. First, there is uncertainty as to the future costs of reparations, including impacts of changes in socio-economic conditions. As can be seen from the above analysis, however, a more important source of uncertainty is that of the probability of flood events, and this is reflected in the range of climate futures used.

Other key sources of uncertainty that have not been fully reflected in the analysis above include:

- the assumption that flood damages occurring in a 1994–5 type winter, and the frequency of this event, are equivalent to those for the October 2000 flood event.
- the assumption that buildings will continue to be preserved and maintained to existing standards until the end of the century.

Implications for adaptation and general conclusions

The restoration costs from flood damage in October 2000 of the two buildings considered here were in practice met as a result of insurance coverage. As with buildings more generally, however, it is clear from the discussion relating to the socio-economic scenarios that insurers' policy towards properties at flood risk may change either independently of climate change or because of climate change. In the case of the latter, insurers may either increase premiums, withdraw coverage or demand that property owners or public authorities take preventative measures e.g. through the creation of flood defences. Indeed the threat of coverage withdrawal or higher premiums may stimulate flood defence creation.

The fact that the two buildings being considered here are of cultural significance does not imply that adaptation measures should be specifically tailored to them. Indeed, changes in insurance policy are likely to be in response to the flood risk to property more generally. Similarly up-grading flood defence systems are likely to be most cost-effective when reducing flood risk to the community of Lewes as a whole, rather than single buildings. Consequently, it does not appear appropriate to consider adaptation measures for the two heritage buildings highlighted here independently of all the other properties which are likely to be included in a cost-benefit analysis of flood risk policies that incorporate climate scenarios.

This case study – focusing as it does on the cost of climate change related flood damage to non-utilitarian structures (cultural objects) – does however, raise some specific issues relating to costed climate impact assessments and adaptation evaluation. These include:

■ Differences between restoration costs and willingness to pay (WTP) values

In this case study it is the restoration costs associated with repairing flood damage that have been used to cost the impacts of climate change. In a cost-benefit appraisal of adaptation, however, restoration of damage caused may be seen as a (reactive) adaptation option itself so that the restoration costs should be included on the cost side of the appraisal. As outlined above, these costs – if committed – represent only a minimum of the true social value of preserving the buildings. Thus, without using non-market or other non-monetary measures we are not able to reflect the full value of cultural objects in the evaluation of adaptation options where these objects may benefit from their implementation. This limitation should therefore be borne in mind both when evaluating flooding adaptation measures and when using such data as a proxy for the welfare costs of climate change impacts.

■ Aggregation

Associated with the first issue, it is clear from the case study that the individual nature and value of cultural objects makes it very difficult to aggregate climate impact costs over a number of cultural object "units". Whilst it may be possible to approximate restoration costs per square metre of floor space on the basis of knowledge of the materials damaged, it seems less likely that the full social value of one building or other cultural object can be straightforwardly aggregated up across a number of units. However, we have not tested this proposition. Indeed, we may find that the uncertainties associated with such an exercise are no greater than those associated with other parts of the impact assessment.

■ Restoration knowledge

One further caveat to the interpretation of restoration costs as a proxy of welfare loss relates to the fact that the loss may be exacerbated by the loss of skilled craftsmen or of particular skills or materials necessary for exact restoration to the original. For example, to replace old wood with new causes a loss to the heritage value of a building that is particularly difficult to quantify.

References

1 Philip Hadley, BCN Limited in a letter dated 22 September 2006 to Ian Wainwright, Ecclesiastical Insurance.

2 The authors gratefully acknowledge the assistance of Pastor Noel Shields of Jireh Chapel in the preparation of this report.

3 Cassar M., (2005) *Climate Change and the Historic Environment Scoping Study Report*, English Heritage and UKCIP.

4 Metroeconomica (2004) *Costing the Impact of Climate Change*. UKCIP, Oxford. Available online at www.ukcip.org.uk.

5 ibid.

Feedback from Dissemination Workshop 1
Glasgow Caledonian University, 7 September 2006

Chair: Neil Ross, Conservation Architect

Following formal presentations of the scientific research, a number of questions were posed by participants, to which a rapporteur responded.

Paul Baker, Glasgow Caldonian University as rapporteur:

How do we measure moisture content of walls?
A number of questions were posed and suggestions given regarding moisture measurements. These have been described in more detail in earlier papers in this publication.

Can non-invasive sensors be used to measure water content? Practical and safety issues exclude some techniques, for example X-rays etc.
Paul Baker referred to work to develop surface electrical resistance measurements which sounds promising.

Can moisture movement through and the wetting and drying of masonry with different salt contents be measured and compared?
Paul Baker suggested that this was possible using combined resistance/ capacitance techniques.

In view of the difficulties of measuring moisture in materials with dowels, can Protimeter™-type devices be relied upon in everyday use?
Paul Baker replied in the affirmative adding that they are probably better for measuring timber moisture contents.

Can an indicator material be found to which correlations with typical historical building materials can be made?
Paul Baker remarked that this was discussed during breakout session, suggesting the possible use of alternative materials to dowels, for example fired clay with controlled porosity.

Is the complexity of new measurement techniques a worthwhile solution to measuring properties in situ?
It depends on what you want! For model validation improved techniques would be particularly valuable.

Finally the rapporteur reported that the suggestions on the kind of measurements basically covered absorptivity and permeability measurements, which are already being carried out.

Ian Ridley, University College London as rapporteur:

In answer to the question, 'How do we apply computer models to historic masonry structure?' the following comments were made:

When will computer modelling lead to a commercially available climate change prediction service (for maintenance managers and owners)?
The new models developed in the project are still research tools and not ready to be used commercially. However Wufi and Energy plus are available commercially and are widely used by Consultant engineering companies and academic institutions.

Can 3 dimensional details be modeled and could gravity be included in future models?
The models have many simplifications, and further complexity could be included, but this possibly would be at the expense of usability and speed of simulation. A useful approach may be to recognise that in certain situations it be necessary to use specialist or niche software, which have the appropriate complexity, and for more general work simpler models may be used.

No two historic buildings will be alike, and therefore it is unlikely that one computer model will be able to take account all aspects all historic buildings
The models will need to be flexible enough to cope with building diversity and certain simplifications and assumptions will need to be made.

It a may be beneficial to find a generic material which would be representative of typical historic building material.

One approach would be to create a library of material properties with advice on the sensitivity of model predictions to material properties and the possible diversity and non-uniformity of historic building materials.

Expand the model to take into account the conditions within rooms that are necessary to maintain and conserve contents and artefacts in museums or historic collections

The internal Room RH and temperature are predicted in the models, and the predictions could be used to assess if the ideal or necessary conditions required to conserve the contents are being achieved. Similarly the conditions for the growth of mould etc could be examined.

Chris Sanders, Glasgow Caledonian University as rapporteur:

The following comments were received in answer to the Breakout Session question: How can climate change effects on historic building moisture properties be predicted?

1. Preventative maintenance of historic buildings is even more important in the light of the increased stresses from the external climate that buildings are likely to experience. The future climate should be taken into account when any maintenance is planned; for example, if gutters etc. are being replaced consideration should be given to installing larger ones, if this is possible.

2. At present, predictions of future wind speed have the lowest confidence however as wind might be expected to have significant effects on the moisture performance of buildings its effects should be studied by modelling sooner rather than later. Two opposite effects of increased wind are possible:
- more driving rain increasing wetting of structures;
- more drying on the outside of walls when it is not raining and inside due to higher ventilation rates.

It should be possible to establish which of these effects will dominate in any building type.

3. Although more wetting and drying of masonry under a more severe climate may not cause damage in itself, it will promote salt movement in many cases, which will cause secondary damage.

4. More information is needed about the performance of materials under climate stresses. It would be useful to set up a database of materials and their performance that could be added to progressively. This would be a resource for the whole conservation community but might be complicated to administer.

5. Driving rain and flooding are not the only effects of moisture on buildings. Milder, more humid winters with greater external vapour pressure, will increase the chances of mould, mildew etc on interior surfaces and soft furnishings. This should be borne in mind when background heating/ventilation of buildings over the winter is considered.

6. Various buildings, which can be regarded as examples of specific building types could be instrumented and monitored to provide early warning of the response of that building type to changes in the climate.

Chris Hawkings, Ecclesiastical Insurance as rapporteur:

The following comments, grouped in three main areas were received in answer to the Breakout Session question: How can natural and forced drying be studied?

1. The need for bench marks against which "ideal" conditions could be measured.
a. Is there ideal moisture content for historic fabric?
b. If so, what is it, and how is this achieved?
c. Does the ideal differ for different types of building materials
d. If this can only be achieved by continuous mechanical intervention can this be justified on environmental grounds?

e. If a building is repaired following saturation, won't the conditions merely return to their normal state anyway after de-humidification is removed?

2. Acceptance that historic buildings are complex.

a. The internal structure of an historic wall is complex. It may consist of an external stone layer with a rubble core mixed with mortar. The transport of moisture through this structure is complex and needs to be studied three dimensionally rather than two dimensionally.

b. Is it possible to separate out the different factors that affect drying and examine each one individually measuring their effects while the others remain constant:

   i.   Humidity

   ii.   Temperature

   iii.   Solar radiation

   iv. CO_2

   v.   Wind

3. Need for more detailed research.

a. Is it possible to work out the density of different types of masonry walls and then pump air through them at different temperatures and relative humidities and measure the effect on the other side of the wall over measured periods of time?

b. Can we determine the thermal/moisture barrier performance of different wall structures?

Chair: Ian Wainwright, Ecclesiastical Insurance

Following formal presentations of the scientific research, a number of questions were posed to participants who responded with comments and further questions as follows:

How do we study moisture movement in historic masonry?

The moisture movement study was very interventive in its nature. Can invasive methods always be justified? It was argued that invasive techniques should only be used where basic observation does not provide the answers.

Moisture doesn't affect stone too much but we need to know how embedded timbers might be affected. Is it easier to measure the moisture in the timbers or the panelling next to the wall?

Knowledge of the history of the building is crucial. The wall may be wet now, but it may always have been so. There is an issue of lack of continuity of care as organisations go through change or if architects/surveyors cease to have long term relationships with buildings.

Should we also look at modern changes in use and increased expectations as part of this exercise? Are our expectations of an historic building too high? We seal them up – fire compartment are created to cope with changed use. Is this the priority and not climate change?

Historic masonry could have been repaired in several interventions over time (but records may not be available). So in any one wall there can be many variables. How can we develop an effective economic tool kit to deal with this without requiring "pepperpot" holes?

Consider presenting some of the data as moisture content (mass) rather than RH – am sure the programme can cope!

We need to know how moisture movement activates contaminants and why salting occurs.

How good is a Protimeter™ at measuring dampness in a wall? Will it give a good first indication?

Built-in sensors for long-term monitoring: What's happening across section of wall for example from the outer surfaces to the interior?

Were alternatives to wooden dowels considered? Probes can be used to measure moisture content – in building research department in universities etc.

Why did you choose wooden dowels with the slow response? There are sensors from Vaisala used to monitor drying on concrete before floor finshes laid. Are there any good?

Have you tried weighing a filter paper applied to the wall for a period of time (assuming no plastic paint interlayer)?

An Infrared survey gives information on the lowering of surface temperature due to evaporation: Have ventilation studies been linked to this?

Study the salt and algae lines and quantities: Brush salts off and remove them from the building on a seasonal basis. Note changes on a database.

Research themes so far restricted to above ground structures. Are there any future possibilities of studying climate change effects on underground structures?

It would be useful for the publication to include a list of actions that may be undertaken by researchers/site managers to collect basic information that would be required for any future analysis of a site.

How can natural and forced drying be studied?

The Building Regulations on airtightness need to be complied with for change of use. Part L of the Building Regulations does apply to historic buildings. How do we deal with this? Natural ventilation is a good thing (if air ventilation is appropriate).

It would be interested to see data from the forced drying experiment at Blickling Hall (graph showing RH of two walls and the room) as absolute moisture content. Was the RH drop in space due to a temperature rise rather than the removal of moisture from the space? Would that be still considered as drying?

If buildings are going to go back to an equilibrium (and/or take a very long time to dry out), how do we explain this to their owners and persuade them to convert them to appropriate uses? Stop complaining that the cellar is damp!

I would like to see a top ten list of key actions of do's & don't's after a severe event. For example, rapid dehumidification in Prague after the 2002 floods led to horrific damage to historic panelling. A simple list saying "dry at over 6m" would be useful!

Private owner paying for 100 days of dehumidification which then in days go back to what it was originally!

Detrimental effects on contents and interiors.

Again, monitoring systems are important – the relationship between conditions and objects.

Carlisle; Boscastle; New Orleans; Prague.

Maintenance regimes: Blickling is a good example. Gutter and outlets need cleaning more regularly. Climatic conditions encourage the growth of lichens/moss etc. which then block small/narrow or moderate outlets. Budgets have to increase significantly to cope with this and the new Health & Safety legislation to gain access.

I have concerns about the term forced 'Drying Out': are we expecting too much by fighting the natural environment that has existed for 100s of years?

The research suggests that forced drying *in situ* needs to be very carefully controlled – laboratory studies require appropriate through-thickness construction.

Is the objective to prove that both will in the long/medium term produce the same equilibrium? Therefore forced drying is an unnecessary use of energy.

Doesn't forced drying accelerate the deterioration process? Aren't we looking forward to more harmonious solutions?

SPAB viewpoints: the outcome of this research emphasises the importance of maintenance. Persuasion with management is needed.

Is 100 pages needed? Unless the publication summarises quite a lot of information that is out there, it will not be useful to have a very lengthy publication.

How do we apply computer models to historic masonry structures?

Simulation must at least have the ability to describe in 2D mortar, joints, voids etc. Drying is not the opposite of wetting! Are the material properties used in models (measured during wetting tests) adequate?

It would be interesting to see air exchange modelled as a variable with wind, air temperature etc. fed into the calculation.

How detailed do construction details need to be for the model? How does one deal with heat flux through windows?

To test computer modelling start with measuring independently (two teams) a recent building built in accordance with current standards. One team measures actual situation, the other generates a computer predictive model.

The modelling programme seemed to be lacking necessary data particularly on building materials and construction techniques.

Research into other building materials to expand "regional" focus as opposed to the international.

Are there plans to develop a model to give a clearer idea of the effects on the interiors of the building – i.e. painted walls/furnishings.

Can the computer models be developed to relate to wall finishes such as medieval wall paintings, timber panels, Victorian tile schemes?

How does this project fit into other previous projects – such as pollution modelling – which also required data on building materials. Are they all going to be brought together at some time?

I felt that one presentation said how difficult it is to properly measure moisture in walls. Another presentation gave very confident computer modelled predictions – can we believe the predictions?

The project forecasts for wall saturation were particularly useful and interesting.

How can climate change effects on historic building moisture properties be predicted?

Will there be any comment (possibly based on computer modelling) on the effects on other wall constructions, eg. Rubble stone set in various mortars; implications of various wall finishes?

Will the presentation of results include prediction of scenarios with lower or medium emissions? This would provide valuable context about the extent we can change things with emission reduction.

Can hourly climate data continue to be obtained after the BETWIXT project ends?

When it is warmer in future summers, will it be sunnier? Or will it be cloudier?

Wind driven rain is an important factor to look at when combined with temperature rises? More laboratory tests should be developed.

We need to use vulnerability assessments – hazard, exposure, sensitivity and adaptive capacity.

We look forward to preventing damage. We need a range of probabilities for which we should be prepare.

We need to look at the impacts on ruins, World Heritage Sites and archaeology etc.

Monitoring for pests as indicators of change in contents and building structures.

What will the effect be of increased moisture and higher temperatures on moulds, rots, insects in buildings and their contents?

How do you propose to link this work with "natural/environmental" concerns for example rare lichen/fungi? Are there linkages/should there be?

We need to look at how maintenance regimes must change and this needs to be built into policy now. It takes time for this to be translated into practice and for budgets to be put into place, for example, churches may need to club together to buy cherry pickers to wash out gutters.

By the use of a barometer and good maintenance.

The report should emphasise the importance of maintenance – particularly for those areas likely to be most affected by climate change.

If increased rain falling on walls – historic walls – is not going to have any significant effect we need to concentrate on the roots, gutters etc. in order to increase the capacity of rainwater goods – by how much?

The findings need to reaffirm the need to get the basics right for example the maintenance regime.

The report must have an introductory section that says WHY this matters.

Could any publicity be prefaced by a 'don't panic' message aimed at volunteers and private owners of historic buildings? I am concerned that many will be overwhelmed at the prospect of repeated flooding, get demoralised and simply give up trying to maintain their buildings.

My concern is that we need people to understand that the research in these subjects will lead us to ask the right questions in order to find the appropriate solutions. We cannot expect "formulas" that will resolve the problem.

Can the 'imponderables' be expressed in the publication i.e. lack of constructive information, and how it might be supplemented by our historical and architectural information of the site?

Can the report be written to be as readable as possible. The challenge should be to make the narrative flow and read easily with as little technical description as possible without sacrificing necessary detail.

Please could the final results be presented in a format that: a) uses language that practitioners, especially architects/surveyors/conservators, can grasp; b) gives people practical guidelines eg. do you clean your gutters, don't try to double their size!

Can the report please include something on what further work is needed/might be undertaken.

This needs to feed into other projects, particularly those aimed at non-building professionals. Linkages could be made to CIRIA, Defra, flood stakeholders etc.

Please include a bibliography with reference information published on the web.

Sarah Staniforth, The National Trust, as rapporteur:

Impact of floods on domestic buildings – homes:
- ■ Cost of dehumidification then returning to equilibrium:
  - Consider the effect of drying out too quickly. Consider the damage to panelling following the 2002 floods in Prague
  - Distinguish between a flood and a damp cellar
- ■ Impact of drying on interiors and contents:
  - Drying out too quickly/slowly drying
  - Need to zoning
- ■ Importance of maintenance:
  - Clean air
  - Gutter clearance
  - Health and Safety
- ■ Ventilation is way of drying:
  - Forced drying waste of energy
  - 'Harmonic' solution
- ■ Part L building Regs:
  - Air tightness required in historic buildings
- ■ Publication:
  - 100 pages may be too long
  - Executive summary
  - Emphasise importance of management

May Cassar, University College London, as rapporteur:

Bob Lowe and Bill Bordass suggested a triage system of traffic lights: red, amber and green representing (i) leave well alone; (ii) remove or (iii) add.

The debate which involved Bob Lowe, Bill Bordass and Sarah Staniforth raised the issue of metrics, ie kPascals versus RH. An explanation is needed about the metrics that are used and this may have to be a note in the publication that should be commissioned to act as a bridge between the scientists who measure moisture (liquid or vapour) in walls and heritage managers who measure RH in indoor environments for collections.

References should include 'Putting it off: how lack of maintenance fails our heritage', published by Maintain Our Heritage, November 2004 as suggested by a participant from Pucell Miller Tritton.

Sarah Staniforth raised the issue of how far the research has concentrated on historic buildings and the impact of flooding and how much on the dynamics of drying out. The publication needs to make this clear.

The publication needs an Executive Summary that gives clear messages from the research. Some of the issues mentioned at the Workshop include:
- Thick masonry walls have a high moisture content anyway. Current rainfall predictions do not indicate significant changes in driving rain effects on the moisture content of historic walls.
- If the summers get drier in the 'far future' (2070–2099), the internal conditions, starting with the internal surfaces of walls (which may include wall paintings) within historic buildings may get drier.